# PRE-ALGEBRA
## ANSWER KEY & TEST BANK

Greg Sabouri
Shawn Sabouri

## Table of Contents

*Pre-Algebra: A Teaching Textbook*™
*Answer Key and Test Bank*
Greg Sabouri and Shawn Sabouri

Copyright © 2005 by Teaching Textbooks, Inc.

Printed in the United States of America.

ISBN: 0-9749036-5-5

Teaching Textbooks, Inc.
P. O. Box 60529
Oklahoma City, OK  73146
www.teachingtextbooks.com

## CHAPTER 1

### Practice 1
a. 26
b. 1,108
c. LXII
d. MMDCCXXXIII
e. XII

### Problem Set 1
1. True
2. False
3. False
4. False
5. True
6. B
7. E
8. B
9. 3
10. 11
11. 28
12. 261
13. 617
14. 1,212
15. XXXVI
16. LXXIII
17. CCVI
18. MMMDCCXXI
19. 2001
20. XXIII

### Practice 2
a. 5,238,446,395,042
b. 5,630,002
c. one hundred fifty million, eighty-eight thousand, three hundred forty-one
d. 9,876,542
e. 34,569

### Problem Set 2
1. True

2. True
3. C
4. E
5. D
6. A
7. B
8. 13
9. 671
10. 1,262
11. 7, 8, 9, 1
12. 4, 8, 6, 2, 3, 5, 7
13. 58,162,840
14. 8,150,276,150,938
15. 27,632
16. 14,311,004
17. forty-six thousand, eight hundred sixty-seven
18. five hundred twenty million, seventy-five thousand, nine hundred ninety-eight
19. 943,210
20. 8,765,432
21. 1,467
22. 12,367

### Practice 3
a. 12,342,000,065
b. two hundred million, five thousand, eight hundred eighty-five
c. 23,579
d. 37,797
e. 569,979

### Problem Set 3
1. D
2. A
3. D
4. 7, 3, 2, 1

5. 8, 0, 3, 2, 5, 1, 4
6. 400,020
7. 2,006,000
8. 14,861,000,047
9. fifty-two thousand, four hundred eighty-eight
10. six hundred million, three thousand, one hundred nineteen
11. 2,378
12. 12,345
13. 10,000,000
14. 34,590
15. 209,000
16. 74
17. 98
18. 789
19. 989
20. 8,489
21. 77,778
22. 84,637
23. 994,136

### Practice 4
a. 1,000,400,000,655
b. 3,855,965
c. 242
d. 290
e. 100,373

### Problem Set 4
1. False
2. True
3. 1, 2, 3, 8
4. 9, 3, 5, 6, 4, 8, 8
5. 8,200,357
6. 9,000,300,000,074
7. forty-three thousand, seven hundred ninety-nine

8. eight hundred million, five hundred ninety-six thousand, twenty-five
9. 75,543,211
10. 887,643,210
11. 5,060,021
12. 5,070,011
13. 65
14. 466
15. 80
16. 151
17. 100
18. 59
19. 190
20. 1,887
21. 9,134
22. 100,453

## Practice 5
a. 6,703,155
b. 5,149,812
c. 160
d. 1,027
e. 24,642

## Problem Set 5
1. False
2. True
3. 9, 9, 9, 9
4. 8, 0, 1, 0, 0, 0, 0
5. 31,450,817
6. 80,014,036, 200,006
7. eighty-eight thousand, nine hundred seventy-five
8. nine hundred thirty-six million, thirty-four thousand, eight hundred forty-nine
9. 8,394,088

10. 8,804,088
11. 1,185,302
12. 6,524
13. 83,496
14. 975,302
15. 1,334
16. 10,774
17. 110
18. 1,528
19. 1,029
20. 672
21. 16,169
22. 2,862
23. 148,028

## Practice 6
a. 3,127,210
b. 31
c. 451
d. 33,128
e. 133 parasites

## Problem Set 6
1. True
2. False
3. False
4. 4, 5, 1, 0
5. 6, 2, 0, 0, 7, 0, 0
6. 40,025,011
7. 17,000,034,006
8. 1,050,023,014,000
9. 5,218,912
10. 5,308,912
11. 7,893,050
12. 7,393,550
13. 1,295
14. 10,684
15. 40,671
16. 1,271
17. 19,157
18. 58
19. 22
20. 133
21. 712
22. 3,225

23. 74,454
24. 132 sunflower seeds

## Practice 7
a. 7,022
b. 36
c. 789
d. 489
e. 175 finger puppets

## Problem Set 7
1. True
2. True
3. 2, 8, 7, 6, 5
4. 4, 5, 8, 9, 3, 2, 3, 9
5. 476,999
6. 60,035,106
7. 900,200,016, 300,450
8. three million, five hundred seventy-eight thousand, four
9. fifty-nine thousand, one
10. 105,875
11. 114,875
12. 38,284,835
13. 550
14. 7,823
15. 135,977
16. 1,637
17. 10,863
18. 70
19. 99,485
20. 29
21. 37
22. 889
23. 389
24. 2,268 pounds

## CHAPTER 2

### Practice 8
a. 3×7 or 7×3
b. 6×2 or 2×6
c. 10 objects
d. 268
e. 11×14 or 14×11

### Problem Set 8
1. True
2. False
3. False
4. True
5. 4, 0, 0, 1
6. 2, 0, 0, 7, 8, 9, 4, 3
7. 50,003
8. 700,400,302
9. 211,000,084
10. 10,000,000,001
11. ninety-nine thousand, eight hundred seventy-five
12. five hundred sixty thousand, one
13. 201,065
14. 39,055,789
15. 4×5 or 5×4
16. 7×3 or 3×7
17. 14×3 or 3×14
18. 27 objects
19. 1,200
20. 10,039
21. 54,257
22. 75,285
23. 29
24. 148
25. 12×17 or 17×12

### Practice 9
a. 100×5 or 5×100
b. 1,200
c. 56,000
d. 180,000
e. 360 minutes

### Problem Set 9
1. True
2. False
3. 18,420
4. 600,134
5. 302,019
6. 3×19 or 19×3
7. 17×100 or 100×17
8. 1,500
9. 60,763
10. 744,482
11. 75,285
12. 29
13. 228
14. 8
15. 45
16. 0
17. 420
18. 5,800
19. 689,000
20. 200,000
21. 6,000
22. 300,000
23. 600 days

### Practice 10
a. 1,200,000
b. 48
c. 2,205
d. 50,526
e. 81 auditions

### Problem Set 10
1. False
2. True
3. 2,003,009
4. 5,000,140,000
5. 10,000
6. 1,000,000
7. 1,000,102
8. 171
9. 130,000,000
10. 313,412
11. 260
12. 147
13. 350
14. 9,600
15. 799,000
16. 80,000
17. 8,000
18. 600,000
19. 86
20. 1,314
21. 19,126
22. 105 free throws

### Practice 11
a. 16×429 or 429×16
b. 3,712
c. 19,075
d. 398,504
e. 10,972 complaints

### Problem Set 11
1. True
2. True
3. 6×8 or 8×6
4. 72×31 or 31×72
5. 28×512 or 512×28
6. 1,800,000
7. 2,779
8. 78,283
9. 1,418
10. 7,664
11. 226
12. 4,312
13. 1,719
14. 6,106
15. 21,328
16. 933
17. 3,432
18. 10,712

19. 516
20. 2,432
21. 25,675
22. 49,608
23. 501,809
24. 7,176 times

## Practice 12
a. $56 \div 7$
b. 6
c. 194,427
d. 147,132
e. 1,800 skirts

## Problem Set 12
1. True
2. False
3. False
4. B
5. C
6. A
7. E
8. $42 \div 7$
9. $72 \div 9$
10. 8
11. 1
12. 594
13. 209
14. 12,767
15. 306
16. 106
17. 6,814
18. 15,247
19. 1,095
20. 1,950
21. 50,034
22. 147,888
23. 281,200
24. 4,350 acorns

## Practice 13
a. 667,509
b. 3,196,441
c. 30

d. 900
e. 3,000 centuries

## Problem Set 13
1. True
2. True
3. 2
4. 1
5. 210,000,000
6. 1,194
7. 12,136
8. 15,798
9. 382
10. 1,229
11. 65,949
12. 14,799
13. 20,088
14. 469,800
15. 560,802
16. 263,408
17. 4,217,468
18. 30
19. 50
20. 5,000
21. 700
22. 2 kumquats

## Practice 14
a. 4,700,000
b. 17,201,880
c. 589
d. 789 R1
e. 78 shawls

## Problem Set 14
1. False
2. True
3. 3,800,000
4. 600
5. 7
6. 202
7. 1,482
8. 20,354
9. 494
10. 970

11. 22,988
12. 38,956
13. 331,000
14. 918,900
15. 80,600
16. 36,985,010
17. 40,003,782
18. 96
19. 69
20. 452
21. 32 R2
22. 452 R5
23. $145

## Practice 15
a. 238,000,000
b. 12,518,493
c. 391
d. 452 R4
e. $85

## Problem Set 15
1. True
2. False
3. False
4. 425,000,000
5. 700
6. 400,000
7. 1,001
8. 1,692
9. 13,020
10. 293
11. 978
12. 34,729
13. 23,907
14. 278,525
15. 708,972
16. 35,784,760
17. 11,262,552
18. 131
19. 680
20. 794 R2
21. 242
22. 318
23. 443 R4

**24.** 1,532 comic books

## Practice 16
  **a.** 1,450
  **b.** Yes
  **c.** Yes
  **d.** 327 R3
  **e.** 180,000 pairs

## Problem Set 16
  **1.** True
  **2.** True
  **3.** True
  **4.** 23,700,000,000
  **5.** 2,380
  **6.** Yes
  **7.** Yes
  **8.** No
  **9.** 13,206
  **10.** 17,140
  **11.** 20,378
  **12.** 379
  **13.** 8,409
  **14.** 32,989
  **15.** 61,380
  **16.** 265,736
  **17.** 6,551,596
  **18.** 34 R3
  **19.** 389
  **20.** 471 R3
  **21.** 323
  **22.** 384 R10
  **23.** 11,850 days

## CHAPTER 3

### Practice 17
a. Yes
b. Yes
c. $\dfrac{1}{4}$
d. 155 R28
e. 15 members

### Problem Set 17
1. True
2. False
3. True
4. True
5. 7,000
6. Yes
7. Yes
8. $\dfrac{1}{3}$
9. 7,302
10. 9,931
11. 20,442
12. 515
13. 1,772
14. 16,631
15. 36,738
16. 592,188
17. 12,467,745
18. 54
19. 532
20. 854 R2
21. 343
22. 137 R29
23. 28 in-laws

### Practice 18
a. Yes
b. $\dfrac{5}{8}$
c. $\dfrac{3}{4}$
d. 265 R10
e. 19 weeks

### Problem Set 18
1. True
2. False
3. No
4. Yes
5. Yes
6. $\dfrac{2}{4}$
7. $\dfrac{6}{11}$
8. $\dfrac{3}{5}$
9. 8,330
10. 1,548
11. 10,966
12. 379
13. 2,334
14. 30,470
15. 69,156
16. 661,692
17. 393,546
18. 38 R2
19. 674
20. 367 R6
21. 273
22. 124 R2
23. 644 days

### Practice 19
a. Yes
b. $\dfrac{5}{4}$
c. 4,470,950
d. 151 R32
e. 35 coconuts

### Problem Set 19
1. True
2. True
3. False
4. Yes
5. $\dfrac{3}{17}$
6. $\dfrac{3}{2}$
7. $\dfrac{4}{7}$
8. 1,107
9. 6,383
10. 19,270
11. 629
12. 659
13. 43,976
14. 6,559
15. 37,772
16. 3,812,380
17. 48 R3
18. 83 R4
19. 146
20. 113
21. 156 R7
22. 17 ounces

### Practice 20
a. <
b. <
c. <
d. $\dfrac{4}{3}$
e. $4,788

### Problem Set 20
1. False
2. False
3. <
4. >
5. <
6. Yes
7. No
8. $\dfrac{11}{7}$
9. 1,527
10. 1,825
11. 16,786
12. 42
13. 528
14. 13,756

15. 25,569
16. 14,768
17. 561,393
18. 76 R3
19. 206 R2
20. 50
21. 69 R6
22. 70 R31
23. $12,600

## Practice 21
a. <
b. Yes
c. $\frac{1}{7}$
d. $\frac{1}{5}$
e. 185 restaurants

## Problem Set 21
1. True
2. False
3. =
4. <
5. Yes
6. Yes
7. $\frac{2}{5}$
8. 21,114
9. 23,801
10. 550
11. 1,828
12. 42,559
13. 56,000
14. 88,494
15. 36,894
16. 54 R4
17. 935
18. 75
19. $\frac{1}{5}$
20. $\frac{1}{3}$

21. $\frac{5}{6}$
22. 15,480 leaflets

## Practice 22
a. <
b. 123 R14
c. $\frac{3}{7}$
d. $\frac{3}{2}$
e. 180 days

## Problem Set 22
1. True
2. True
3. <
4. >
5. No
6. Yes
7. 17,169
8. 26,641
9. 4,935
10. 4,327
11. 47,857
12. 20,900
13. 7,942
14. 386,106
15. 49 R3
16. 456 R4
17. 50 R12
18. $\frac{3}{5}$
19. $\frac{5}{11}$
20. $\frac{7}{5}$
21. 72 days

## Practice 23
a. Yes
b. Yes

c. $\frac{1}{3}$
d. $\frac{7}{8}$
e. 19 papers

## Problem Set 23
1. True
2. True
3. True
4. >
5. >
6. Yes
7. Yes
8. $\frac{1}{2}$
9. 17,046
10. 12,274
11. 2,465
12. 1,288
13. 3,390
14. 4,773
15. 23,548
16. 382,200
17. 43 R1
18. 394 R4
19. 83 R4
20. $\frac{7}{6}$
21. $\frac{1}{2}$
22. $\frac{5}{8}$
23. 298 comments

## CHAPTER 4

### Practice 24

a. $\dfrac{9}{2}$

b. 9

c. $\dfrac{7}{9}$

d. 1

e. $\dfrac{2}{3}$

### Problem Set 24

1. False
2. False
3. =
4. =
5. Yes
6. $\dfrac{2}{2}$
7. 17,685
8. 96,176
9. 168
10. 22,110
11. 13,630
12. 44,912
13. 438,845
14. 45 R3
15. 201
16. 66 R14
17. $\dfrac{4}{3}$
18. $\dfrac{2}{3}$
19. 4
20. $\dfrac{4}{5}$
21. $\dfrac{6}{7}$
22. 1
23. $\dfrac{1}{5,000,000}$ meters

### Practice 25

a. $\dfrac{8}{25}$

b. 3

c. $\dfrac{1}{3}$

d. $\dfrac{1}{6}$

e. $\dfrac{7}{9}$

### Problem Set 25

1. True
2. True
3. =
4. <
5. 13,238
6. 80,243
7. 5,054
8. 73,704
9. 52,548
10. 343,476
11. 751 R2
12. 83 R13
13. $\dfrac{1}{9}$
14. $\dfrac{1}{2}$
15. $\dfrac{8}{9}$
16. $\dfrac{7}{9}$
17. 2
18. $\dfrac{1}{2}$
19. $\dfrac{3}{5}$
20. $\dfrac{2}{11}$
21. $\dfrac{1}{3}$
22. $\dfrac{9}{13}$ of the beaker

### Practice 26

a. $\dfrac{1}{4}$

b. $\dfrac{13}{12}$

c. $\dfrac{4}{9}$

d. $\dfrac{8}{21}$

e. $\dfrac{1}{2}$ of a bottle

### Problem Set 26

1. True
2. False
3. =
4. <
5. 10,053
6. 3,808
7. 117,481
8. 79,828
9. 62,915
10. 42,596
11. 256,795
12. 583
13. 345 R10
14. $\dfrac{2}{9}$
15. $\dfrac{1}{7}$
16. $\dfrac{5}{4}$
17. $\dfrac{4}{7}$
18. $\dfrac{1}{2}$
19. $\dfrac{7}{6}$
20. $\dfrac{2}{9}$
21. $\dfrac{3}{8}$

22. $\dfrac{7}{15}$

23. $\dfrac{3}{8}$ of a box

21. $\dfrac{1}{24}$

22. $\dfrac{5}{6}$ of the weekend

18. $\dfrac{33}{56}$

19. $\dfrac{5}{3}$

20. $\dfrac{3}{8}$ of the cows

## Practice 27
a. 24
b. 56
c. $\dfrac{32}{21}$
d. $\dfrac{1}{30}$
e. $\dfrac{7}{36}$ of the can

## Practice 28
a. 36
b. $\dfrac{25}{7}$
c. $2\dfrac{5}{6}$
d. $\dfrac{4}{3}$
e. $\dfrac{3}{4}$ of the cows

## Problem Set 27
1. True
2. True
3. 14,140
4. 55,639
5. 88,772
6. 10,355
7. 16,072
8. 219,184
9. 1982 R1
10. 203
11. $\dfrac{3}{5}$
12. $\dfrac{5}{6}$
13. 6
14. 12
15. 72
16. 1
17. $\dfrac{5}{9}$
18. $\dfrac{29}{24}$
19. $\dfrac{3}{11}$
20. $\dfrac{3}{10}$

## Problem Set 28
1. True
2. False
3. 12,412
4. 8,294
5. 27,058
6. 61,285
7. 3,089 R18
8. 218,232
9. $\dfrac{4}{15}$
10. $\dfrac{4}{3}$
11. 84
12. 42
13. $\dfrac{13}{3}$
14. $\dfrac{65}{9}$
15. $3\dfrac{1}{7}$
16. $2\dfrac{3}{4}$
17. $\dfrac{13}{15}$

## CHAPTER 5

### Practice 29

a. $4\frac{1}{2}$

b. $\frac{29}{24}$

c. $\frac{15}{4}$

d. 10

e. 4 turkeys

### Problem Set 29

1. True
2. True
3. 17,381
4. 22,058
5. 12,029
6. 45,936
7. 315 R2
8. 229,338
9. $\frac{1}{2}$
10. $\frac{5}{7}$
11. 120
12. 90
13. $\frac{47}{5}$
14. $\frac{113}{10}$
15. $4\frac{1}{7}$
16. $6\frac{1}{3}$
17. $\frac{16}{9}$
18. $\frac{35}{6}$
19. $\frac{29}{20}$
20. 6

21. $\frac{16}{3}$
22. 6
23. 9 trays

### Practice 30

a. $\frac{31}{24}$

b. 4

c. 65

d. 51

e. 52 tablecloths

### Problem Set 30

1. True
2. False
3. 14,555
4. 31,453
5. 37,696
6. 215 R34
7. $\frac{3}{8}$
8. $\frac{4}{9}$
9. 16
10. 52
11. $\frac{53}{6}$
12. $\frac{63}{5}$
13. $7\frac{1}{2}$
14. $5\frac{3}{4}$
15. $\frac{27}{20}$
16. $\frac{35}{12}$
17. 5
18. 7
19. 22
20. 36
21. 124

22. 64 bottle caps

### Practice 31

a. $\frac{1}{10}$

b. $\frac{7}{15}$

c. $\frac{1}{50}$

d. $\frac{5}{16}$

e. $\frac{1}{18}$ of a gallon

### Problem Set 31

1. True
2. False
3. 18,187
4. 41,586
5. 785
6. 343,368
7. $\frac{1}{2}$
8. $\frac{6}{17}$
9. 10
10. 36
11. $\frac{7}{8}$
12. $\frac{7}{40}$
13. $\frac{11}{2}$
14. $\frac{5}{2}$
15. $\frac{19}{15}$
16. $\frac{21}{8}$
17. $\frac{12}{11}$

18. $\dfrac{1}{12}$

19. $\dfrac{5}{6}$

20. 56

21. $\dfrac{2}{27}$

22. $\dfrac{3}{25}$

23. $\dfrac{1}{12}$ of a whole pound

## Practice 32

a. $\dfrac{3}{5}$

b. $\dfrac{3}{4}$

c. $\dfrac{2}{5}$

d. $\dfrac{5}{14}$

e. $\dfrac{1}{80}$ of the estate

## Problem Set 32

1. True
2. True
3. 18,739
4. 32,987
5. 1,042
6. 687,463
7. $\dfrac{1}{3}$
8. $\dfrac{2}{3}$
9. 40
10. 210
11. $\dfrac{7}{3}$
12. $\dfrac{5}{8}$

13. $\dfrac{38}{35}$

14. $\dfrac{10}{3}$

15. $\dfrac{17}{12}$

16. $\dfrac{5}{3}$

17. $\dfrac{2}{3}$

18. $\dfrac{2}{3}$

19. 660

20. $\dfrac{7}{20}$

21. $\dfrac{2}{3}$

22. $\dfrac{1}{160}$ of the estate

## Practice 33

a. $\dfrac{1}{6}$

b. $\dfrac{15}{4}$

c. 3

d. 100

e. $\dfrac{1}{40}$ of the pie

## Problem Set 33

1. True
2. True
3. 13,349
4. 31,927
5. 838,090
6. 966 R1
7. $\dfrac{7}{3}$
8. $\dfrac{4}{9}$

9. $\dfrac{5}{7}$

10. $\dfrac{1}{9}$

11. $\dfrac{13}{20}$

12. $\dfrac{19}{12}$

13. $\dfrac{20}{3}$

14. 14

15. $\dfrac{1}{6}$

16. $\dfrac{2}{5}$

17. $\dfrac{1}{12}$

18. $\dfrac{6}{5}$

19. 2
20. 51
21. 200
22. $\dfrac{1}{35}$ of the pitcher

# CHAPTER 6

## Practice 34
a. 300
b. 0.3
c. 0.6
d. 3.8
e. $\dfrac{1}{6}$ of a pizza slice

## Problem Set 34
1. True
2. True
3. 16,989
4. 41,859
5. 839,108
6. 762 R5
7. 1
8. $\dfrac{1}{4}$
9. $\dfrac{89}{84}$
10. $\dfrac{11}{24}$
11. $\dfrac{41}{4}$
12. 48
13. $\dfrac{2}{55}$
14. $\dfrac{1}{6}$
15. $\dfrac{5}{2}$
16. $\dfrac{1}{14}$
17. 450
18. 0.1
19. 0.4
20. 14.5
21. $\dfrac{1}{174}$ of the water cooler

## Practice 35
a. 14.09
b. $\dfrac{3}{2}$
c. 2.625
d. 0.2
e. $\dfrac{1}{10}$ of the racers

## Problem Set 35
1. True
2. False
3. 8,239
4. 31,933
5. 1,222,440
6. 2,054 R8
7. $\dfrac{5}{6}$
8. $\dfrac{17}{28}$
9. $\dfrac{67}{72}$
10. $\dfrac{31}{10}$
11. $\dfrac{1}{11}$
12. $\dfrac{1}{14}$
13. $\dfrac{10}{9}$
14. $\dfrac{9}{5}$
15. 64
16. 525
17. 24.07
18. $\dfrac{7}{3}$
19. 10.375
20. 0.25
21. $\dfrac{1}{36}$ of the villains

## Practice 36
a. 2.007
b. 0.6
c. 33.349
d. 595.652
e. $\dfrac{1}{8}$ of the recipes

## Problem Set 36
1. True
2. True
3. 12.07
4. 3.005
5. 0.4
6. 68.75
7. 6.52
8. 766.86
9. 22.288
10. 720.141
11. 79,488
12. 547
13. $\dfrac{7}{8}$
14. $\dfrac{2}{15}$
15. $\dfrac{89}{12}$
16. $\dfrac{34}{5}$
17. $\dfrac{1}{3}$
18. $\dfrac{35}{2}$
19. $\dfrac{1}{6}$
20. 198
21. 10
22. $\dfrac{1}{24}$ of the fans

## Practice 37
a. 0.189
b. 6.625

c. 934.98
d. 14.37
e. $\dfrac{1}{30}$ of the outfielders

## Problem Set 37

1. True
2. False
3. 0.142
4. 7.23
5. 10.375
6. 68.57
7. 3.82
8. 965.28
9. 24.45
10. 90.925
11. 222,040
12. 701 R10
13. $\dfrac{9}{11}$
14. $\dfrac{130}{21}$
15. $\dfrac{29}{4}$
16. $\dfrac{9}{5}$
17. $\dfrac{1}{15}$
18. $\dfrac{1}{16}$
19. 12
20. 60
21. 84
22. $\dfrac{1}{14}$ of the islanders

## Practice 38

a. 0.023
b. $13.70
c. $0.83
d. 132.315
e. $9,131.03

## Problem Set 38

1. True
2. True
3. 0.17
4. 0.052
5. 18.0003
6. $17.35
7. $0.64
8. 18.01
9. 20.89
10. 411.39
11. 136.261
12. 1,296,000
13. 784
14. 3
15. $\dfrac{1}{18}$
16. $\dfrac{11}{8}$
17. $\dfrac{7}{2}$
18. $\dfrac{7}{2}$
19. $\dfrac{9}{5}$
20. $\dfrac{1}{6}$
21. 12
22. $9,066.15

## Practice 39

a. 0.0409
b. 2.926
c. 1.4222
d. 9,715.2
e. $14.85

## Problem Set 39

1. True
2. False
3. 0.0101
4. 0.22
5. $11.74

6. $1.31
7. 78.07
8. 220 or 220.0
9. 19.117
10. 833.304
11. 22.1256
12. 2.376
13. 1.5941
14. 5,234
15. 3,020.4
16. $\dfrac{4}{7}$
17. $\dfrac{11}{36}$
18. 8
19. $\dfrac{2}{15}$
20. $\dfrac{1}{6}$
21. 96
22. 900
23. $10.20

## Practice 40

a. 0.32
b. 25.41
c. 23.7
d. 52
e. 16 bottles

## Problem Set 40

1. True
2. True
3. 0.9
4. 0.04
5. 24.03
6. 91.877
7. 24.54
8. 28.793
9. 78.1
10. 1,843.91
11. 5,232
12. 26.2575
13. 48.3

14. $\dfrac{5}{4}$

15. $\dfrac{25}{33}$

16. $\dfrac{1}{14}$

17. $\dfrac{3}{8}$

18. $\dfrac{2}{5}$

19. $\dfrac{1}{7}$

20. 21
21. 7 bottles

## Practice 41
a. 120.5
b. 783.625
c. 232.75
d. $\dfrac{10}{3}$
e. 112 potatoes

## Problem Set 41
1. True
2. True
3. 318.22
4. 7.183
5. 1,475.4
6. 131.5
7. 25.925
8. 915.625
9. 58.14
10. 253.375
11. 12.072
12. $\dfrac{19}{28}$
13. $\dfrac{8}{15}$
14. 81
15. $\dfrac{3}{2}$

16. $\dfrac{1}{14}$

17. $\dfrac{5}{22}$

18. 32

19. $\dfrac{21}{2}$

20. 47 skateboards

## Practice 42
a. 1243.25
b. $\dfrac{1}{27}$
c. 0.875
d. $\dfrac{59}{200}$
e. 94.5 centimeters

## Problem Set 42
1. True
2. False
3. 54.761
4. 52.73
5. 69.27
6. 257.43
7. 4.3
8. 723.84
9. 125.2
10. 40.2584
11. 1,308.75
12. $\dfrac{29}{20}$
13. $\dfrac{1}{14}$
14. 20
15. $\dfrac{1}{10}$
16. $\dfrac{1}{8}$
17. 0.4
18. 0.375
19. $\dfrac{23}{100}$

20. $\dfrac{29}{200}$
21. 1.9 pounds

## Practice 43
a. 220
b. $435.\overline{6}$
c. $0.\overline{4}$
d. 0.29
e. 0.012 inches

## Problem Set 43
1. False
2. True
3. 1,041.79
4. 21.515
5. 977.1
6. 64.05
7. 302
8. 29.2658
9. $470.\overline{6}$
10. 35.287
11. $\dfrac{50}{9}$
12. $\dfrac{1}{6}$
13. $\dfrac{2}{3}$
14. 35
15. $\dfrac{2}{7}$
16. 0.35
17. $0.\overline{1}$
18. $\dfrac{31}{50}$
19. $\dfrac{1}{125}$
20. 0.44
21. 0.58
22. 0.9 inches

## CHAPTER 7

### Practice 44
a. 0.14
b. 0.93
c. $\dfrac{17}{1,000}$
d. 6
e. 47 pennies

### Problem Set 44
1. True
2. False
3. 175.17
4. 489.01
5. 12.159
6. 80.625
7. 3.05
8. 379.47
9. $703.\overline{6}$
10. 885.6
11. $\dfrac{13}{2}$
12. $\dfrac{29}{5}$
13. 4
14. $\dfrac{2}{3}$
15. 0.6
16. 0.57
17. 0.79
18. $\dfrac{4}{5}$
19. $\dfrac{29}{1,000}$
20. 6
21. 21
22. 32 pennies

### Practice 45
a. $211.8\overline{3}$
b. 0.64
c. $\dfrac{16}{25}$
d. 162
e. 30 clowns

### Problem Set 45
1. True
2. True
3. 572.55
4. 4.284
5. 232.2
6. 56
7. 9.1205
8. $314.1\overline{6}$
9. 85.5
10. $\dfrac{5}{14}$
11. $\dfrac{25}{24}$
12. 57
13. 27
14. 0.875
15. 0.83
16. 0.82
17. $\dfrac{11}{100}$
18. $\dfrac{8}{25}$
19. $\dfrac{701}{1,000}$
20. 42
21. 176
22. 20 sailors

### Practice 46
a. 0.92
b. 6.8
c. 8.1
d. 0.12
e. $24.50

### Problem Set 46
1. True

2. False
3. 938.14
4. 47.175
5. 14.843
6. 84
7. 378.717
8. 48.5
9. $253.\overline{2}$
10. $\dfrac{1}{9}$
11. $\dfrac{5}{6}$
12. $\dfrac{1}{4}$
13. 2
14. 0.0625
15. 0.42
16. $\dfrac{3}{250}$
17. $\dfrac{13}{20}$
18. 60
19. 8.4
20. 10.4
21. 0.15
22. $41.25

### Practice 47
a. $\dfrac{7}{2}$
b. 0.085
c. 0.24
d. 1.8
e. $180.19

### Problem Set 47
1. True
2. False
3. 98.61
4. 391.93
5. 73.5
6. 283.96
7. 422.6

8. $\dfrac{38}{35}$

9. $\dfrac{5}{2}$

10. 9

11. $\dfrac{1}{33}$

12. 0.45

13. 0.89

14. $\dfrac{41}{200}$

15. $\dfrac{5}{2}$

16. 0.15

17. 0.065

18. 77

19. 0.48

20. 4.06

21. $0.52

## Practice 48

a. 0.55125

b. $\dfrac{7}{25}$

c. $\dfrac{1}{30}$

d. 40.32

e. i.) $96.25
   ii.) $101.54

## Problem Set 48

1. True
2. True
3. True
4. 23.965
5. 44.57
6. 18.624
7. 85.$\overline{3}$
8. $\dfrac{1}{5}$
9. $\dfrac{1}{2}$

10. $\dfrac{1}{12}$

11. $\dfrac{5}{3}$

12. 0.07

13. 0.16

14. $\dfrac{17}{200}$

15. $\dfrac{21}{5}$

16. 0.144

17. 0.75125

18. $\dfrac{19}{50}$

19. $\dfrac{4}{75}$

20. 607.6

21. 39

22. i.) $97.50
    ii.) $103.84

## Practice 49

a. 1.2

b. 180

c. 30%

d. 25%

e. 60%

## Problem Set 49

1. 69.58
2. 376.5
3. 0.09375
4. 982.75
5. 38.48
6. $\dfrac{11}{6}$
7. $\dfrac{87}{10}$
8. $\dfrac{1}{3}$
9. 24
10. 0.58
11. 1.25

12. $\dfrac{3}{125}$

13. $\dfrac{12}{25}$

14. 0.67

15. 0.981

16. 330

17. 32.9

18. 73.125

19. 25%

20. 80%

21. 75%

## Practice 50

a. $\dfrac{54}{25}$

b. 1.1

c. 6.3

d. 50%

e. $33\dfrac{1}{3}\%$

## Problem Set 50

1. False
2. True
3. 61.16
4. 10.27
5. 0.73
6. 64.5
7. 7.896
8. $\dfrac{9}{8}$
9. $\dfrac{4}{7}$
10. 60
11. 8
12. 0.85
13. 1.17
14. $\dfrac{9}{20}$
15. $\dfrac{103}{25}$
16. 0.6225

**17.** 1.2
**18.** 140
**19.** 2.1
**20.** 25%
**21.** $26\frac{2}{3}\%$

# CHAPTER 8

## Practice 51

a. $\dfrac{29}{10}$

b. $\dfrac{7}{50}$

c. $\dfrac{9}{400}$

d. 4%

e. 88%

## Problem Set 51

1. True
2. False
3. 1,327.97
4. 461.1
5. 17.575
6. 8.7
7. 57.3
8. $\dfrac{7}{8}$
9. $\dfrac{1}{2}$
10. $\dfrac{2}{3}$
11. $\dfrac{3}{22}$
12. 0.18
13. 0.06
14. $\dfrac{41}{50}$
15. $\dfrac{27}{10}$
16. $\dfrac{13}{50}$
17. $\dfrac{13}{400}$
18. 600
19. 5.2
20. 8%
21. 90%

## Practice 52

a. 0.14
b. 1.85
c. 5.25
d. 15%
e. 80 people

## Problem Set 52

1. True
2. True
3. False
4. 1,261.18
5. 4.095
6. 35,700
7. $2,526.\overline{6}$
8. 1.768
9. $\dfrac{17}{6}$
10. $\dfrac{4}{5}$
11. $\dfrac{3}{10}$
12. $\dfrac{1}{2}$
13. 0.875
14. 0.29
15. $\dfrac{19}{20}$
16. $\dfrac{1}{5}$
17. 0.181
18. 2.25
19. 40
20. 5.58
21. 20%
22. 375 people

## Practice 53

a. 60 inches
b. 210 feet
c. 10,560 yards
d. 32%
e. 108 inches

## Problem Set 53

1. True
2. False
3. 117,284
4. 16.46
5. 16.25
6. 35.25
7. 668.75
8. $\dfrac{23}{20}$
9. $\dfrac{1}{2}$
10. $\dfrac{3}{2}$
11. 15
12. 1.8
13. 0.33
14. 0.128
15. 3.4
16. 72 inches
17. 240 feet
18. 3,520 yards
19. 105.6
20. 64%
21. 84 inches

## Practice 54

a. 0.0045
b. 288 inches
c. 31,680 feet
d. 1.5 miles
e. 3,542,880 feet

## Problem Set 54

1. 126.68
2. 3,431
3. $189.\overline{7}$
4. 3,796
5. 14.6
6. 2
7. $\dfrac{1}{12}$

8.  $\dfrac{4}{3}$

9.  $\dfrac{2}{7}$

10. 3.5

11. 0.17

12. $\dfrac{1}{20}$

13. $\dfrac{7}{50}$

14. 0.085

15. 0.0075

16. 324 inches

17. 26,400 feet

18. 2.5 miles

19. 19.2

20. 12.5%

21. 4,224,000 feet

## Practice 55
a.  360 inches
b.  3.2 miles
c.  405,504 inches
d.  50%
e.  0.25 yards

## Problem Set 55
1.  True
2.  True
3.  672
4.  47.16
5.  28.14
6.  293.75
7.  23,790
8.  1
9.  $\dfrac{7}{2}$
10. $\dfrac{3}{10}$
11. $\dfrac{1}{4}$
12. 0.625
13. 0.83

14. 0.7725
15. 5.0
16. 432 inches
17. 3.5 miles
18. 456,192 inches
19. 3.5
20. 20%
21. $0.8\overline{3}$ yards

## Practice 56
a.  14 yards
b.  7,920 inches
c.  432
d.  119 inches
e.  12 bed sheets

## Problem Set 56
1.  True
2.  False
3.  628
4.  30.58
5.  8.712
6.  56.25
7.  $\dfrac{3}{8}$
8.  $\dfrac{13}{10}$
9.  $\dfrac{7}{3}$
10. $\dfrac{5}{6}$
11. 0.45
12. 0.93
13. $\dfrac{99}{100}$
14. $\dfrac{4}{5}$
15. 17 yards
16. 37,488 feet
17. 15,840 inches
18. 306
19. 180
20. 148 inches

21. 56 days

## Practice 57
a.  4.5 yards
b.  29,040 feet
c.  28
d.  3.25 miles
e.  i.) $66  ii.) $69.63

## Problem Set 57
1.  True
2.  False
3.  8,892
4.  4.921
5.  991.2
6.  23.5
7.  14.45
8.  $\dfrac{49}{12}$
9.  $\dfrac{2}{9}$
10. 1
11. $\dfrac{9}{2}$
12. 0.6
13. 0.55
14. 408 inches
15. 3.5 yards
16. 23,760 feet
17. 10
18. 82
19. 4.35
20. 2.5 miles
21. i.) $225
    ii.) $241.88

## Practice 58
a.  0.0065
b.  288 inches
c.  24.75 feet
d.  7.5 miles

e.  1,459.25 feet

or $1,459\frac{1}{4}$ feet

## Problem Set 58

1. True
2. True
3. D
4. C
5. A
6. 40.625
7. 61,394
8. 0.0696
9. 93.125
10. $\frac{5}{8}$
11. $\frac{3}{10}$
12. 15
13. 36
14. 0.525
15. 0.0075
16. 150 feet
17. 276 inches
18. 23.75 feet
19. 11.45 miles
20. 20.75 feet or
    $20\frac{3}{4}$ feet

## Practice 59

a.  240 feet
b.  5,000 centimeters
c.  0.415 kilometers
d.  2.92 hectometers
e.  2,000 centimeters

## Problem Set 59

1. False
2. False
3. D
4. C
5. B
6. 6,201

7. 6.932
8. 2,108
9. 5.345
10. $\frac{25}{3}$
11. $\frac{1}{36}$
12. $\frac{3}{7}$
13. 3
14. 0.02
15. 0.64
16. 300 feet
17. 8,000 centimeters
18. 0.245 kilometers
19. 3.74 hectometers
20. 2,400 centimeters

## Practice 60

a.  3.8 meters
b.  196.85 inches
c.  14.22 yards
d.  70%
e.  3,502.80 miles

## Problem Set 60

1. 85.75
2. 138.3
3. 73.35
4. 672
5. $\frac{2}{3}$
6. $\frac{7}{12}$
7. $\frac{3}{8}$
8. $\frac{1}{14}$
9. $\frac{13}{20}$
10. $\frac{1}{250}$
11. 0.074

12. 1.24
13. 11,541 feet
14. 4.2 meters
15. 314.96 inches
16. 18.59 yards
17. 40
18. 19.5
19. 80%
20. 870.11 miles

## CHAPTER 9

### Practice 61
a. 396 inches
b. 750 centimeters
c. 10.16 centimeters
d. 3.66 meters
e. 20.32 centimeters

### Problem Set 61
1. True
2. True
3. D
4. D
5. 47,580
6. 3.625
7. 1.302
8. 281.25
9. $\dfrac{2}{3}$
10. $\dfrac{1}{15}$
11. $\dfrac{1}{12}$
12. 4
13. 0.212
14. 3.75
15. 432 inches
16. 860 centimeters
17. 7.62 centimeters
18. 4.57 meters
19. 292
20. 25%
21. 91.44 centimeters

### Practice 62
a. 103 meters
b. 1,296 square inches
c. 7 square yards
d. 77
e. 51.875 square feet

### Problem Set 62
1. True
2. True
3. A
4. E
5. 5.979
6. 424
7. 36.18
8. 16.48
9. $\dfrac{13}{6}$
10. $\dfrac{2}{15}$
11. 12
12. 42
13. 0.035
14. 0.98
15. 26.5 feet or $26\dfrac{1}{2}$ feet
16. 115 meters
17. 1,152 square inches
18. 8 square yards
19. 292
20. 95
21. 980 square feet

### Practice 63
a. 6,195,200 square yards
b. 1,400 square decimeters
c. 3 square yards
d. 6.7 square meters
e. 290,000 square centimeters

### Problem Set 63
1. True
2. True
3. E
4. A
5. 16.89
6. 39,955
7. 0.3857
8. 523.5
9. $\dfrac{3}{4}$
10. $\dfrac{11}{6}$
11. $\dfrac{3}{22}$
12. $\dfrac{8}{27}$
13. 0.33
14. 0.7
15. 9.75 miles or $9\dfrac{3}{4}$ miles
16. 42 hectometers
17. 9,292,800 square yards
18. 1,200 square decimeters
19. 4 square yards
20. 8.2 square meters
21. 1,080,000 square centimeters

### Practice 64
a. 6 hectometers
b. 33.02 centimeters
c. 2.5 square feet
d. 1.42 square kilometers
e. 12 cubic feet

### Problem Set 64
1. True
2. False
3. True
4. A
5. E
6. 17.5
7. 4.56
8. 78.3

9. $57.\overline{7}$
10. $\dfrac{13}{15}$
11. 3
12. $\dfrac{1}{12}$
13. 30
14. $\dfrac{3}{5}$
15. $\dfrac{13}{25}$
16. 2.5 feet
17. 5 hectometers
18. 24
19. 27.94 centimeters
20. 3.5 square feet
21. 1.75 square kilometers
22. 840,000 cubic feet

## Practice 65
a. 70%
b. 10,368 cubic inches
c. 7 cubic yards
d. 40,000 square centimeters
e. 9,000 cubic yards

## Problem Set 65
1. True
2. True
3. B
4. B
5. 8,706
6. 0.289
7. 200
8. 181.2
9. $\dfrac{7}{10}$
10. $\dfrac{2}{9}$
11. 80

12. $\dfrac{14}{3}$
13. 0.005
14. 1.89
15. 1.5 miles or $1\dfrac{1}{2}$ miles
16. 5 kilometers
17. 80%
18. 8,640 cubic inches
19. 8 cubic yards
20. 30,000 square centimeters
21. 6 cubic yards

## Practice 66
a. 432 inches
b. 28 pints
c. 837 cubic feet
d. 4.827 kilometers
e. 7 pints

## Problem Set 66
1. True
2. True
3. D
4. E
5. 56.29
6. 4.072
7. 161.35
8. 2,530
9. $\dfrac{11}{8}$
10. $\dfrac{8}{5}$ or $1\dfrac{3}{5}$
11. $\dfrac{1}{10}$
12. $\dfrac{3}{2}$
13. 0.875
14. $0.\overline{54}$
15. 84
16. 7.98

17. 540 inches
18. 24 pints
19. 756 cubic feet
20. 3.218 kilometers
21. 5 pints

## Practice 67
a. 25%
b. 75 square yards
c. 260 deciliters
d. 5 gallons
e. 1,400,000 cubic decimeters

## Problem Set 67
1. False
2. True
3. B
4. E
5. C
6. 26,833
7. 0.242
8. 56.73
9. 73.25
10. $\dfrac{2}{3}$
11. $\dfrac{17}{20}$
12. 25
13. 18
14. 0.45
15. $0.0\overline{5}$
16. 60
17. 34
18. 30%
19. 85 square yards
20. 240 deciliters
21. 4 gallons
22. 200,000,000 cubic decimeters

## CHAPTER 10

### Practice 68
a. Algebra problem
b. 5
c. 1
d. $\frac{3}{5}$
e. 20 deciliters

### Problem Set 68
1. True
2. True
3. True
4. A
5. B
6. D
7. A
8. 16.53
9. 10.2
10. 7.218
11. 89
12. $\frac{8}{15}$
13. $\frac{1}{7}$
14. $\frac{2}{5}$
15. $\frac{14}{5}$
16. Algebra problem
17. Arithmetic problem
18. Algebra problem
19. 4
20. 1
21. $\frac{3}{7}$
22. 50 deciliters

### Practice 69
a. 18,000 cubic millimeters
b. 4.2 miles
c. $25 + x = 62$
d. $x - 17 = 34$
e. 18 employees

### Problem Set 69
1. True
2. True
3. False
4. D
5. D
6. C
7. 1,614
8. 84.25
9. $\frac{99}{8}$ or $12\frac{3}{8}$
10. $\frac{4}{3}$ or $1\frac{1}{3}$
11. $0.\overline{1}$
12. 0.1875
13. 14,000 cubic millimeters
14. 3.8 miles
15. 9,792 square inches
16. $23 + x = 51$
17. $x - 19 = 27$
18. $\frac{1}{2} \times x = 14$
19. $\frac{1}{4}$
20. 2
21. 111
22. 6 pounds

### Practice 70
a. 384 fluid ounces
b. 3.7 square dekameters
c. add 145
d. 26
e. 15 gallons

### Problem Set 70
1. True
2. True
3. True
4. A
5. E
6. D
7. 2,095
8. 536.5
9. $\frac{17}{5}$ or $3\frac{2}{5}$
10. 0
11. 4
12. $\frac{2}{7}$
13. 0.8275
14. 1.05
15. 256 fluid ounces
16. 4.9 square dekameters
17. Subtract 92
18. Add 115
19. 23
20. 49
21. 24
22. 12 ounces

### Practice 71
a. Divide by 14
b. Multiply by 25
c. 31
d. 40.15
e. 64 cubic inches

### Problem Set 71
1. True
2. False
3. A
4. C
5. D
6. 23.46
7. 68.7
8. $\frac{1}{6}$

9. $\dfrac{13}{9}$

10. $\dfrac{3}{20}$

11. $\dfrac{2}{11}$

12. 8,700 millimeters
13. 8 square feet
14. Divide by 17
15. Multiply by 35
16. 14.8
17. 103
18. 23
19. 189
20. 53.3
21. 1,024 cubic inches

## Practice 72
a. 2,300 milliliters
b. No
c. 43.9
d. 8
e. 117 women

## Problem Set 72
1. True
2. False
3. D
4. B
5. 586.5
6. 46.75
7. $5\dfrac{3}{4}$ or $\dfrac{23}{4}$
8. $\dfrac{3}{5}$
9. 0.375
10. $0.1\overline{6}$
11. 3,800 milliliters
12. 18 yards
13. No
14. Yes
15. 65.9

16. $\dfrac{4}{5}$
17. 9
18. $\dfrac{1}{7}$
19. 48
20. $\dfrac{4}{3}$
21. 1,244 participants

## Practice 73
a. $7x$
b. $\dfrac{x}{3}$
c. 600 square decimeters
d. No
e. $\dfrac{5}{2}$ gallons or $2\dfrac{1}{2}$ gallons

## Problem Set 73
1. True
2. True
3. A
4. C
5. 12,787
6. 1.566
7. $\dfrac{5}{6}$
8. $\dfrac{11}{21}$
9. 0.78
10. 1.0375
11. $8x$
12. $\dfrac{x}{2}$
13. 400 square decimeters
14. 20 yards

15. Subtract $\dfrac{1}{3}$
16. Multiply by 4.5
17. No
18. Yes
19. 0.7
20. $\dfrac{7}{9}$
21. 4,260
22. $\dfrac{7}{4}$ gallons or $1\dfrac{3}{4}$ gallons

## Practice 74
a. $3 \cdot 5$ or $(3)(5)$ or $3(5)$ or $(3)5$
b. 15
c. 48.6
d. 8
e. 480 pounds

## Problem Set 74
1. False
2. True
3. B
4. A
5. 0.1472
6. $317.\overline{3}$
7. $15\dfrac{3}{5}$ or $\dfrac{78}{5}$
8. $1\dfrac{1}{4}$ or $\dfrac{5}{4}$
9. 1.4
10. $0.\overline{09}$
11. 900 centimeters
12. 2 miles
13. $2 \cdot 6$ or $(2)(6)$ or $2(6)$ or $(2)6$
14. Add $\dfrac{4}{9}$
15. Divide by 1,250

16. 12
17. 45
18. $\dfrac{3}{8}$
19. $\dfrac{3}{2}$
20. 18
21. 20 feet tall

## Practice 75
a. 0.035 square meters
b. 2,600 milliliters
c. $\dfrac{1}{10}$
d. $\dfrac{2}{3}$
e. $745

## Problem Set 75
1. A
2. B
3. 193.7
4. 19.4
5. $\dfrac{4}{3}$
6. $\dfrac{1}{14}$
7. 0.1225
8. 1.5
9. 0.028 square meters
10. 1,200 milliliters
11. 15$x$
12. $\dfrac{x}{3}$
13. Yes
14. Yes
15. 22.2
16. 13
17. 10.5
18. $\dfrac{2}{3}$

19. $\dfrac{1}{12}$
20. $\dfrac{7}{6}$
21. $5,200

## Practice 76
a. 3,200 square decimeters
b. 60 miles
c. 360 miles
d. $\dfrac{1}{4}$
e. 8 hours

## Problem Set 76
1. True
2. True
3. D
4. B
5. 100.3
6. $7,108.\overline{3}$
7. $\dfrac{13}{12}$
8. $\dfrac{3}{14}$
9. 0.25
10. $0.1\overline{3}$
11. 13 yards
12. 4,200 square decimeters
13. $\dfrac{1}{3}x$
14. $\dfrac{x}{7}$
15. Multiply by 24
16. 80 miles
17. 330 miles
18. 14
19. 198
20. $\dfrac{5}{6}$
21. 32 hours

## CHAPTER 11

### Practice 77
a. 40 quarts
b. 6 miles
c. No
d. $-5$
e. $70

### Problem Set 77
1. True
2. True
3. 23.46
4. 68.7
5. $\dfrac{5}{7}$
6. $\dfrac{1}{12}$
7. 48 quarts
8. 5 miles
9. No
10. No
11. Subtract 158
12. 90 miles
13. 20 miles
14. $-3$
15. $-8$
16. $-12$
17. $\dfrac{3}{5}$
18. 51
19. $\dfrac{1}{2}$
20. 9
21. $450

### Practice 78
a. 84
b. 18 inches
c.

d. $\dfrac{7}{4}$
e. 0.75 hours

### Problem Set 78
1. True
2. True
3. True
4. 20,945
5. 231
6. $\dfrac{1}{2}$
7. $\dfrac{1}{24}$
8. 45
9. 70
10. 3,300 miles
11. 28 inches
12.

13.

14. $-6$
15. $-16$
16. $-1$
17. $\dfrac{5}{8}$
18. 22
19. 14.95
20. $\dfrac{5}{12}$
21. 0.25 hours

### Practice 79
a. 59 dekameters
b. 30 miles
c. $-20$
d. $\dfrac{1}{6}$
e. $60,000

### Problem Set 79
1. False
2. True
3. 90,565
4. 3,627
5. 10
6. 25
7. 432 inches
8. 75 dekameters
9. Add 5,924
10. 10 miles
11. 45 miles
12.

13.

14. 6
15. $-4$
16. $-12$
17. $-17$
18. $+2,000$ or 2,000
19. $\dfrac{3}{10}$
20. 4
21. 100.9
22. $\dfrac{1}{4}$
23. $125,000

### Practice 80
a. $-8$
b. $+5$ or 5
c.

d.

e. 37 mph

## Problem Set 80

1. True
2. False
3. 1.785
4. 66
5. $10\frac{1}{3}$ or $\frac{31}{3}$
6. $1\frac{4}{5}$ or $\frac{9}{5}$
7. 0.3
8. $0.\overline{8}$
9. 32
10. 11.6
11. +35 or 35
12. $-3$
13. $-1$
14. $-5.7$
15. $-6$
16. +7 or 7
17. $-9$
18.

19.

20. 12
21. 6.8
22. 83.2
23. 19 mph

## Practice 81

a. 3.5 miles
b. $-\frac{1}{5}$
c. 1
d. $-23$
e. i.) $900
   ii.) $954

## Problem Set 81

1. True
2. True
3. 34.558
4. 8.16
5. $\frac{2}{5}$
6. $\frac{1}{8}$
7. 5,400 millimeters
8. 2.5 miles
9. 160 miles
10. 50 inches
11. 3
12. $-\frac{1}{4}$
13. $-11$
14. $-7$
15. $-9$
16. 8
17. 3
18. $-19$
19. 1
20. 27
21. 217.2
22. i.) $400
    ii.) $420

## Practice 82

a. $-1$
b. 62
c. $-32$
d. 12
e. 20%

## Problem Set 82

1. True
2. True
3. 29.25
4. $139.1\overline{6}$
5. $\frac{13}{12}$
6. $\frac{11}{21}$
7. 0.32

8. 0.54125
9. 195
10. $\frac{1}{8}$
11. $-42$
12. 4
13. $-1$
14. $-16$
15. $-6$
16. 73
17. $-24$
18. $-35$
19. 27
20. 11.6
21. 19
22. $\frac{4}{11}$
23. 40%

## Practice 83

a. 300 square yards
b. $\frac{6}{7}$
c. $-9$
d. 6
e. $20.95

## Problem Set 83

1. True
2. True
3. 17,187
4. 362.50
5. 21
6. $\frac{1}{18}$
7. 80 hectometers
8. 200 square yards
9. $-23$
10. 25
11. 14
12. $-18$
13. $\frac{4}{5}$

14. $-54$
15. $-60$
16. 28
17. $-6$
18. $-8$
19. 5
20. $\dfrac{3}{5}$
21. 228
22. 115.54
23. $65.75

## Practice 84

a. $-20$
b. 57
c. 16
d. 27
e. 14 mph

## Problem Set 84

1. True
2. True
3. 34.188
4. 519.2
5. $\dfrac{4}{5}$
6. $\dfrac{13}{18}$
7. $0.0\overline{5}$
8. $0.1\overline{3}$
9. $-49$
10. 0
11. 71
12. $-2$
13. $-80$
14. 14
15. $-21$
16. $-10$
17. $-5$
18. 59
19. 12
20. $\dfrac{7}{3}$

21. 15
22. 24
23. 2 mph

## Practice 85

a. 12
b. $-27$
c. $-13$
d. 45
e. 450 lifeguards

## Problem Set 85

1. 1.294
2. 8.62
3. $\dfrac{1}{4}$
4. $\dfrac{4}{3}$
5. 108 miles
6. 12,000 miles
7. $-40$
8. $-100$
9. 10
10. $-22$
11. $-94$
12. $-78$
13. 104
14. $-3$
15. $-14$
16. 21
17. 11
18. $-35$
19. $-19$
20. 48
21. 475 referees

## Practice 86

a. 27,648 cubic inches
b. Yes
c. $-16.2$
d. $-76$
e. 16 mph

## Problem Set 86

1. 285.18
2. 2,595
3. $\dfrac{13}{8}$
4. $\dfrac{8}{15}$
5. 56 quarts
6. 24,192 cubic inches
7. $-129$
8. 64
9. $-21$
10. 40
11. $-91$
12. 95
13. $-3$
14. 7
15. Yes
16. Yes
17. $-23.6$
18. $-408$
19. 11
20. $-68$
21. 65 mph

## Practice 87

a. Yes
b. Yes
c. $-14.1$
d. $-20$
e. 30%

## Problem Set 87

1. True
2. True
3. 111,469
4. 1,204
5. $\dfrac{1}{6}$
6. 40
7. $-220$
8. $-69$
9. $-11$

10. $-41$
11. $-10$
12. $-376$
13. $-2$
14. 9
15. Yes
16. Yes
17. $\dfrac{7}{6}$
18. $-16.8$
19. $-24.6$
20. $-15$
21. 9
22. 40%

19. 63
20. 42
21. 12.5
22. i.) $605
    ii.) $635.25

## Practice 88

a. No
b. Yes
c. 120
d. 48
e. i.) $48
   ii.) $50.88

## Problem Set 88

1. 4.4467
2. 31.55
3. $\dfrac{5}{8}$
4. $1\dfrac{2}{5}$ or $\dfrac{7}{5}$
5. 0.0225
6. 0.462
7. $-37$
8. 2
9. 4
10. $-4$
11. $-180$
12. 266
13. $-11$
14. $-7$
15. No
16. Yes
17. 23
18. 161

# CHAPTER 12

## Practice 89
- a. 21
- b. 18
- c. $5 \cdot 6 + 4$
- d. $(2 + 7) \cdot 4$
- e. 0.8 hours

## Problem Set 89
1. True
2. True
3. True
4. 103.41
5. 27.46
6. 1,008 inches
7. 12.5 meters
8. $-1$
9. 35
10. 22
11. $-134$
12. $-84$
13. 35
14. $-3$
15. 7
16. 19
17. 14
18. $3 \cdot 2 + 5$
19. $(5 + 9) \cdot 3$
20. 34
21. 24
22. $-108$
23. $-2$
24. 0.6 hours

## Practice 90
- a. 15
- b. $5 \cdot 6 - (-9)$
- c. $5x + 4 = 24$
- d. $3(x - 7) = -15$
- e. $90

## Problem Set 90
1. $\dfrac{1}{4}$
2. $\dfrac{3}{2}$
3. 1.2
4. $0.\overline{81}$
5. $-62$
6. $-4$
7. 3.5
8. $-21$
9. $-42$
10. 81
11. $-4$
12. 9
13. Yes
14. No
15. $-6$
16. 24
17. $7 \cdot 4 - (-3)$
18. $2(4 - 12)$
19. $3x + 7 = 31$
20. $4(x - 9) = -20$
21. $\dfrac{1}{10}$
22. 98
23. 64
24. $115

## Practice 91
- a. 6
- b. $\dfrac{20}{4} - 3$
- c. $\dfrac{7 + 8}{5}$
- d. $7(x - 11) = 56$
- e. 11 gallons

## Problem Set 91
1. True
2. True
3. 6 feet
4. 147 miles
5. $-100$
6. $-58$
7. 11
8. $-60$
9. $-44$
10. 0
11. $-10$
12. 7
13. 14
14. 4
15. 5
16. $3 \cdot 6 - 8$
17. $\dfrac{14}{2} - 5$
18. $\dfrac{5 + 11}{8}$
19. $5x + 3 = 18$
20. $3(x - 6) = 45$
21. $\dfrac{7}{5}$
22. $\dfrac{1}{20}$
23. $-68$
24. 7 bars

## Practice 92
- a. $14 - 8 \cdot 3$
- b. $\dfrac{x}{4} - 11 = 32$
- c. $\dfrac{x + 8}{3} = 27$
- d. $-6$
- e. 0.4%

## Problem Set 92
1. $\dfrac{4}{7}$
2. $\dfrac{1}{6}$
3. 0.57
4. 1.32
5. $-42$
6. 13

7. 46
8. $-67$
9. $-36$
10. 99
11. $-3$
12. 4
13. 5
14. $-33$
15. $4(-5+13)$
16. $\dfrac{14-2}{3}$
17. $21-7\cdot6$
18. $2x-6=16$
19. $\dfrac{x}{5}-14=21$
20. $\dfrac{x+9}{2}=30$
21. $\dfrac{11}{21}$
22. $-153$
23. $-4$
24. $0.5\%$

## Practice 93

a. $\dfrac{x}{-6}+24=15$
b. $14(x-3)=70$
c. 7
d. 11
e. 580 mph

## Problem Set 93

1. True
2. False
3. $-72$
4. $-9$
5. 31
6. $-92$
7. 65
8. $-2$
9. 7
10. 14
11. 16

12. 4
13. $-6(7-25)$
14. $\dfrac{28+17}{-9}$
15. $\dfrac{x}{-8}+22=13$
16. $12(x-4)=60$
17. $-\dfrac{3}{8}$
18. $-22$
19. $-17$
20. $-10$
21. 6
22. 18
23. 28 mph

## Practice 94

a. $90-\dfrac{20}{-4}$
b. $\dfrac{x+17}{3}=49$
c. 52
d. 92
e. $16

## Problem Set 94

1. 46.08
2. $892.\overline{5}$
3. 3
4. 86
5. 21
6. $-112$
7. $-8$
8. 1
9. Yes
10. Yes
11. $-14$
12. 3
13. $-2$
14. $-4(8)+18$
15. $100-\dfrac{36}{-6}$
16. $2x-25=38$

17. $\dfrac{x+13}{9}=54$
18. 10
19. $-15$
20. $4\dfrac{1}{2}$ or $\dfrac{9}{2}$
21. $-90$
22. 36
23. 31
24. $48

## Practice 95

a. 16.25 feet
b. $\dfrac{14-8}{3}$
c. $22(x-14)=88$
d. 3
e. 19

## Problem Set 95

1. True
2. True
3. 110.40
4. 17.07
5. 6 yards
6. 13 feet
7. $-1$
8. 17
9. 11
10. $-72$
11. $-5$
12. 8
13. 2
14. $-40$
15. $3(6+9)$
16. $\dfrac{12-7}{5}$
17. $\dfrac{x}{-12}+3=4$
18. $24(x-18)=72$
19. $-12$
20. 9
21. 17

**22.** 5

**23.** 6

**24.** 33

## Practice 96

**a.** $3x + 17$

**b.** $7x + (-4)$

**c.** 4

**d.** $-2$

**e.** 0.625%

## Problem Set 96

**1.** True

**2.** False

**3.** $\dfrac{1}{6}$

**4.** 44

**5.** 0

**6.** 61

**7.** $-48$

**8.** 9

**9.** $-5$

**10.** $-7$

**11.** 20

**12.** $-14$

**13.** $6 \cdot 5 - 18$

**14.** $\dfrac{-11 + 3}{2}$

**15.** $7x + 8$

**16.** $4x + 14$

**17.** $6x + (-5)$

**18.** 88

**19.** 24

**20.** $-5$

**21.** 9

**22.** $-6$

**23.** 0.125%

## CHAPTER 13

### Practice 97
a. $-2(x+7)=36$
b. $8x$
c. $2$
d. $3$
e. 750 meters per second

### Problem Set 97
1. True
2. True
3. True
4. 351 miles
5. 18 inches
6. 7
7. $-200$
8. $-117$
9. 6
10. $-12$
11. 10
12. $\dfrac{x}{-7}-11=53$
13. $-3(x+5)=40$
14. $5x+5$
15. $9x$
16. $-\dfrac{1}{6}$
17. 12
18. 34
19. $-9$
20. 3
21. 2
22. 120 meters per second

### Practice 98
a. $4x$
b. 5
c. 8
d. 6
e. 35

### Problem Set 98
1. True
2. True
3. $0.\overline{6}$
4. $0.01$
5. $-37$
6. $-70$
7. 46
8. $-2$
9. 13
10. 28
11. $31-\dfrac{16}{4}$
12. $6(15+8)$
13. $2x+(-3)$
14. $12x$
15. $6x$
16. $36.24$
17. 14
18. 9
19. 3
20. 6
21. 7
22. 21

### Practice 99
a. $9x$
b. $2x$
c. $-8$
d. $-7$
e. 6

### Problem Set 99
1. True
2. True
3. $\dfrac{11}{10}$
4. $5\dfrac{3}{4}$ or $\dfrac{23}{4}$
5. 33
6. $-16$
7. $-54$
8. $-5$

9. 12
10. 4
11. $\dfrac{x-14}{2}=-1$
12. $10x+6=27$
13. $15x$
14. $5x$
15. $6x$
16. $\dfrac{7}{6}$
17. 4
18. $-1$
19. 7
20. $-9$
21. $-2$
22. 5

### Practice 100
a. 36 square feet
b. $-14x$
c. 7
d. $-5$
e. 2 hours

### Problem Set 100
1. True
2. True
3. 1,700
4. 651
5. 14,000 millimeters
6. 18 square feet
7. $-84$
8. 5
9. $-6$
10. $-2$
11. 10
12. $-63$
13. $\dfrac{-7+(-3)}{5}$
14. $16\cdot 2-21$
15. $2x+13$
16. $18x$
17. $-16x$
18. 14

**19.** 30
**20.** 5
**21.** 11
**22.** $-8$
**23.** 5 hours

## Practice 101

**a.** $-4x$
**b.** 4
**c.** $-5$
**d.** $-8$
**e.** 4 hours

## Problem Set 101

**1.** $\dfrac{1}{8}$
**2.** 12
**3.** $-6$
**4.** $-7$
**5.** 9
**6.** $-64$
**7.** 15
**8.** 11
**9.** 70
**10.** $9x - 7 = 10$
**11.** $\dfrac{x-2}{14} = -33$
**12.** $4x + 3$
**13.** $5x$
**14.** $-6x$
**15.** 14
**16.** 2
**17.** $-40$
**18.** 5
**19.** $-3$
**20.** $-7$
**21.** 2 hours

## Practice 102

**a.** $-7x$
**b.** 2
**c.** 5
**d.** 3

**e.** 8

## Problem Set 102

**1.** True
**2.** True
**3.** 14.411
**4.** 3,287
**5.** $-50$
**6.** $-151$
**7.** $-132$
**8.** 7
**9.** $-19$
**10.** $-8$
**11.** $\dfrac{15}{3} + 21$
**12.** $-5(6-4)$
**13.** $25x + 16$
**14.** $11x$
**15.** $-5x$
**16.** $-2$
**17.** 7
**18.** $-20$
**19.** 3
**20.** 6
**21.** 1
**22.** 2

## Practice 103

**a.** $\dfrac{2}{3}$
**b.** $-2x$
**c.** $\dfrac{4}{5}$
**d.** $-2$
**e.** 5 hours

## Problem Set 103

**1.** 0.42
**2.** 0.7525
**3.** 104.5
**4.** $\dfrac{7}{12}$
**5.** 14

**6.** 18
**7.** $-6$
**8.** $-30$
**9.** $-39$
**10.** 0
**11.** $\dfrac{x}{4} + 26 = 89$
**12.** $-7(x-3) = 21$
**13.** $x + 5$
**14.** $9x$
**15.** $-3x$
**16.** 5
**17.** 60
**18.** 2
**19.** $-9$
**20.** $\dfrac{2}{5}$
**21.** $-1$
**22.** 4 hours

# CHAPTER 14

## Practice 104
a. 19,536 feet
b. $\dfrac{5x}{11}$
c. $\dfrac{1}{5x}$
d. 6
e. 6 hours

## Problem Set 104
1. False
2. True
3. 57 meters
4. 12,672 feet
5. 19
6. $-39$
7. $-3$
8. $-5$
9. 8
10. 6
11. $\dfrac{31-4}{9}$
12. $-3(8)+11$
13. $7x+7$
14. $9x$
15. $\dfrac{2x}{7}$
16. $\dfrac{1}{7x}$
17. $\dfrac{x}{7}$
18. 11
19. $\dfrac{5}{3}$
20. $-9$
21. 2
22. 4
23. 8 hours

## Practice 105
a. $\dfrac{3}{7}$
b. $\dfrac{1}{9}$
c. $-\dfrac{1}{7}$
d. $-3$
e. 3 hours

## Problem Set 105
1. 0.01
2. $0.\overline{2}$
3. $-\dfrac{3}{5}$
4. 133
5. $-98$
6. $-4$
7. 23
8. $-42$
9. $-3x+15=29$
10. $\dfrac{x-7}{20}=-100$
11. $-2x$
12. $3x$
13. $\dfrac{2}{5}$
14. $\dfrac{1}{4}$
15. $\dfrac{4}{9x}$
16. $-27$
17. $-30$
18. $-5$
19. 9
20. $-\dfrac{1}{9}$
21. $-2$
22. 4 hours

## Practice 106
a. $\dfrac{x+7}{2}$
b. $\dfrac{x-3}{2}$
c. $\dfrac{2}{5}$
d. $-\dfrac{6}{5}$
e. 18

## Problem Set 106
1. True
2. True
3. 1,228.54
4. 0.1523
5. $-13$
6. 4
7. $-35$
8. 9
9. 16
10. 3
11. $20(-7+6)$
12. $\dfrac{-42}{6}-8$
13. $9x$
14. $-1x$ or $-x$
15. $\dfrac{1}{8}$
16. $\dfrac{3x}{2}$
17. $\dfrac{x+4}{3}$
18. $\dfrac{x-3}{2}$
19. 5
20. $-39$
21. $\dfrac{4}{3}$
22. $-\dfrac{7}{6}$
23. 48

## Practice 107

a. $\dfrac{3}{x+4}$

b. $\dfrac{1}{7}$

c. $-11$

d. $-\dfrac{2}{7}$

e. 4 hours

## Problem Set 107

1. 637
2. $\dfrac{345}{2}$ or 172.5
3. $-138$
4. $-43$
5. 80
6. $-1$
7. 35
8. $-63$
9. $\dfrac{x}{8}-37=-91$
10. $-13(x+4)=50$
11. $4x+28$
12. $15x$
13. $\dfrac{3}{x}$
14. $\dfrac{1}{5}$
15. $\dfrac{x-2}{3}$
16. $\dfrac{2}{x+1}$
17. $\dfrac{1}{6}$
18. 14
19. $-8$
20. $-12$
21. $-\dfrac{2}{9}$
22. 2 hours

## Practice 108

a. $\dfrac{3}{4}$

b. $\dfrac{1}{12}$

c. $\dfrac{x}{4}$

d. $-3$

e. 3 hours

## Problem Set 108

1. True
2. False
3. $0.6$
4. $0.\bar{1}$
5. $-7$
6. 20
7. $-81$
8. 15
9. $-2$
10. 5
11. $(-7)(16)+22$
12. $\dfrac{11-4}{-3}$
13. $10x+(-6)$
14. $-13x$
15. $\dfrac{7}{x+11}$
16. $\dfrac{2}{3}$
17. $\dfrac{1}{9}$
18. $\dfrac{x}{7}$
19. $-11$
20. $-8$
21. $-2$
22. 4 hours

## Practice 109

a. $-60$

b. $\dfrac{7}{12}$

c. $\dfrac{1}{8}$

d. $\dfrac{4}{3}$

e. 11 seconds

## Problem Set 109

1. 63 miles
2. 5 inches
3. $-12$
4. $-18$
5. 20
6. $-24$
7. $-16$
8. 40
9. $14x+23=101$
10. $\dfrac{x-41}{-5}=26$
11. $76x$
12. $9x$
13. $\dfrac{3}{x+5}$
14. $\dfrac{5}{9}$
15. $\dfrac{4}{3}$
16. $\dfrac{3}{10}$
17. $\dfrac{1}{6}$
18. $\dfrac{2}{3}$
19. $-5$
20. 4
21. 7
22. 4 seconds

## Practice 110

a. $\dfrac{4}{7}$

**b.** $\dfrac{2}{9x}$

**c.** $\dfrac{17}{5x}$

**d.** $\dfrac{13}{21x}$

**e.** 10

## Problem Set 110

1. False
2. True
3. 70.38
4. 2,854.5
5. $-19$
6. $-39$
7. $-54$
8. 4
9. 13
10. 11
11. $3(12+21)$
12. $\dfrac{42}{7}+5$
13. $\dfrac{x+7}{3}$
14. $\dfrac{4}{5}$
15. $\dfrac{1}{4}$
16. $\dfrac{5}{12x}$
17. $\dfrac{4}{x}$
18. $\dfrac{14}{3x}$
19. $\dfrac{23}{6x}$
20. $-7$
21. $-2$
22. 14

## Practice 111

**a.** $\dfrac{5}{6x}$

**b.** $\dfrac{1}{x}$

**c.** $\dfrac{5x}{9}$

**d.** 2

**e.** 2 hours

## Problem Set 111

1. 0.035
2. 1.82
3. $-17$
4. $-3$
5. $-31$
6. $-120$
7. 19
8. 28
9. $5(x-7)=-3$
10. $\dfrac{x}{9}+28=40$
11. $19x$
12. $-10x$
13. $\dfrac{2x}{15}$
14. $\dfrac{1}{2}$
15. $\dfrac{1}{3x}$
16. $\dfrac{7}{8x}$
17. $\dfrac{1}{x}$
18. $\dfrac{5x}{6}$
19. 7
20. $-5$
21. 1
22. 4 hours

## CHAPTER 15

### Practice 112

a. 64

b. $5^7$

c. $\dfrac{3}{8}$

d. $-\dfrac{13}{5x}$

e. 20 minutes

### Problem Set 112

1. True
2. True
3. 83
4. $-13$
5. $-60$
6. $-37$
7. 4
8. 16
9. 243
10. $9^2$
11. $4^6$
12. $(5)(-19)-22$
13. $\dfrac{6+14}{-3}$
14. $\dfrac{x-1}{3}$
15. $\dfrac{3}{4}$
16. $\dfrac{3x}{8}$
17. $\dfrac{5}{12}$
18. $\dfrac{9x}{13}$
19. $-\dfrac{11}{7x}$
20. 27
21. 9
22. 15 minutes

### Practice 113

a. $8.3\times10^{13}$

b. $8^3$

c. $x$

d. 0

e. 9 seconds

### Problem Set 113

1. True
2. False
3. $8\times10^9$
4. $5.7\times10^{13}$
5. $-76$
6. 3
7. 11
8. 35
9. 49
10. 625
11. $9^5$
12. $7^3$
13. $26x+15=305$
14. $\dfrac{x-4}{8}=0$
15. $7x+20$
16. $-23x$
17. $\dfrac{1}{6}$
18. $\dfrac{2}{3x}$
19. $\dfrac{8}{3x}$
20. $x$
21. 2
22. 0
23. 4 seconds

### Practice 114

a. $3.4\times10^{11}$

b. 216

c. 49

d. $\dfrac{x-5}{3}$

e. 12

### Problem Set 114

1. True
2. True
3. $2\times10^6$
4. $5.6\times10^{11}$
5. $-80$
6. $-9$
7. 14
8. 5
9. 40
10. 512
11. 16
12. $4^5$
13. $8^9$
14. $7(22+16)$
15. $\dfrac{42}{6}+19$
16. $\dfrac{3}{5}$
17. $\dfrac{x-7}{2}$
18. $\dfrac{5}{4x}$
19. $\dfrac{13}{10x}$
20. 28
21. 3
22. 17

### Practice 115

a. 6

b. $7x^2$

c. $14x^5$

d. $\dfrac{5}{13}$

e. 2 hours

### Problem Set 115

1. True
2. True
3. $9\times10^4$
4. $1.8\times10^9$

5. $-4$
6. $7$
7. $2$
8. $15$
9. $144$
10. $11$
11. $3(x-29)=41$
12. $\dfrac{x}{20}+52=98$
13. $17x$
14. $9x^2$
15. $11x^5$
16. $\dfrac{x}{4}$
17. $\dfrac{3}{8}$
18. $\dfrac{17}{6x}$
19. $-\dfrac{1}{10x}$
20. $-2$
21. $\dfrac{6}{11}$
22. 5 hours

## Practice 116
a. 1,152 square inches
b. $-8x^4$
c. $6^{12}$
d. $x^8$
e. 7 minutes

## Problem Set 116
1. True
2. True
3. 480 dekameters
4. 2,304 square inches
5. $-43$
6. $-124$
7. $4$
8. $512$
9. $80$

10. $3\cdot 7-15$
11. $\dfrac{14-8}{2}$
12. $\dfrac{3}{4x}$
13. $\dfrac{3}{2}$
14. $\dfrac{5x}{8}$
15. $-\dfrac{18}{5x}$
16. $12x^3$
17. $-9x^4$
18. $4^{11}$
19. $x^6$
20. $6$
21. $-33$
22. 12 hours

## Practice 117
a. $\dfrac{8x}{15}$
b. $-\dfrac{7}{6x}$
c. $56x^7$
d. $\dfrac{13}{5}$
e. 8 seconds

## Problem Set 117
1. $2\times10^{11}$
2. $9.3\times10^7$
3. $12$
4. $0$
5. $18$
6. $144$
7. $79$
8. $8x+(-14)=95$
9. $\dfrac{x-3}{24}=17$
10. $\dfrac{1}{2}$

11. $\dfrac{3x}{5}$
12. $\dfrac{13}{14x}$
13. $-\dfrac{9}{4x}$
14. $19x^2$
15. $3x^8$
16. $x^{10}$
17. $x^{14}$
18. $36x^7$
19. $20x^{16}$
20. $-40$
21. $\dfrac{5}{2}$
22. 3 seconds

## Practice 118
a. $\dfrac{x}{6}$
b. $-42x^{13}$
c. $x^3$
d. $5$
e. $34

## Problem Set 118
1. True
2. True
3. $1.1\overline{6}$
4. $0.04$
5. $9$
6. $16$
7. $3(8+4)$
8. $\dfrac{28}{7}-12$
9. $\dfrac{1}{x}$
10. $\dfrac{2}{25x}$
11. $\dfrac{4}{5x}$

12. $\dfrac{x}{35}$

13. $5x + (-5)$

14. $-4x^5$

15. $19x^7$

16. $x^{14}$

17. $16x^8$

18. $-20x^{16}$

19. $4^5$

20. $x^6$

21. $-4$

22. $6$

23. $\$28$

## Practice 119

a. $\dfrac{7}{20}$

b. $x^2$

c. $\dfrac{x^3}{6}$

d. $3$

e. $14$

## Problem Set 119

1. $8 \times 10^3$

2. $6.5 \times 10^{17}$

3. $343$

4. $\dfrac{5}{12}$

5. $72$

6. $-8$

7. $63$

8. $5$

9. $7(x - 28) = 0$

10. $\dfrac{x}{50} + 41 = -183$

11. $\dfrac{1}{8}$

12. $12$

13. $30x$

14. $11x^4$

15. $x^8$

16. $45x^6$

17. $-48x^{10}$

18. $\dfrac{3}{5}$

19. $x^4$

20. $\dfrac{x^5}{7}$

21. $14$

22. $2$

23. $26$

## Practice 120

a. $-8x^4$

b. $\dfrac{x^5}{6}$

c. $6$

d. $4$

e. $21$ hours

## Problem Set 120

1. True

2. True

3. $11$

4. $64$

5. $12 \cdot 2 - 16$

6. $\dfrac{5 + 94}{33}$

7. $\dfrac{8}{9x}$

8. $\dfrac{2}{3x}$

9. $27x^5$

10. $-5x^9$

11. $x^{19}$

12. $-18x^{12}$

13. $x^9$

14. $x^2$

15. $x^3$

16. $\dfrac{x^4}{5}$

17. $5$

18. $2$

19. $3$

20. $-4$

21. $33$

22. $9$ hours

## Practice 121

a. $x^3$

b. $3$

c. $8$

d. $27$

e. $20\%$

## Problem Set 121

1. True

2. True

3. $-9$

4. $-5$

5. $7$

6. $81$

7. $-4x + 29 = 45$

8. $\dfrac{x - 3}{17} = -11$

9. $x + 5$

10. $-54x$

11. $x^{13}$

12. $30x^8$

13. $\dfrac{3}{2}$

14. $x^2$

15. $x^3$

16. $\dfrac{x^5}{3}$

17. $7$

18. $2$

19. $9$

20. $64$

21. $-3$

22. $72$

23. $25\%$

## ADDITIONAL TOPICS

### Practice 122

a. $-\dfrac{1}{6x}$

b. 3

c. $x^7$

d. 81

e. 2 hours

### Problem Set 122

1. True
2. False
3. $7 \times 10^9$
4. $3.18 \times 10^7$
5. $6(42 + 17)$
6. $\dfrac{18}{3} - 5$
7. $\dfrac{3x}{4}$
8. $-\dfrac{1}{10x}$
9. $13x^4$
10. $5x^7$
11. $x^2$
12. 6
13. $x$
14. $36x^{19}$
15. $x^8$
16. 10
17. 5
18. 7
19. 16
20. 9
21. 8
22. 1 hour

### Practice 123

a. 1

b. $x^4$

c. $x^5$

d. $\dfrac{11}{4}$

e. 13 hours

### Problem Set 123

1. True
2. False
3. 312 miles
4. 60 feet
5. 56
6. 96
7. $10(x - 2) = 18$
8. $\dfrac{x}{5} + 22 = 350$
9. $17x$
10. $2x + 2$
11. $x^4$
12. 1
13. 1
14. $x^3$
15. $x^6$
16. $\dfrac{5x}{12}$
17. $x^4$
18. 3
19. 3
20. 6
21. 64
22. $\dfrac{4}{7}$
23. $\dfrac{8}{3}$
24. 4 hours

### Practice 124

a. $-5x^2$

b. $\dfrac{x}{3}$

c. 3

d. $-\dfrac{5}{6}$

e. 750 meters per second

### Problem Set 124

1. True
2. True
3. 1,094.06
4. 14.05
5. $3 \cdot 6 - 29$
6. $\dfrac{7 + 8}{3}$
7. $\dfrac{8}{9x}$
8. $\dfrac{1}{3x}$
9. $-7x^2$
10. $9x^3$
11. $x^{12}$
12. $-50x^{13}$
13. $x^6$
14. 1
15. $x^8$
16. $\dfrac{x}{2}$
17. 9
18. 2
19. 3
20. 4
21. $-2$
22. $-\dfrac{4}{5}$
23. 3 meters per second

### Practice 125

a. 4.3 tons

b. 73,600 ounces

c. $x^4$

d. $\dfrac{9}{4}$

e. 1.5 pounds

## Problem Set 125

1. True
2. True
3. 608 ounces
4. 5.2 tons
5. 48,000 ounces
6. $7x + 16 = -31$
7. $\dfrac{x - 54}{3} = 26$
8. $5x$
9. $4x + 19$
10. $x$
11. $x^2$
12. $x^8$
13. $156x^7$
14. $\dfrac{6}{x}$
15. $x^5$
16. 7
17. 2
18. 5
19. 16
20. 3
21. $\dfrac{7}{3}$
22. 2.5 pounds

8. $\dfrac{24}{2} - 59$
9. $\dfrac{3x}{5}$
10. $\dfrac{17}{15x}$
11. $-11x^4$
12. $19x^5$
13. $x^{14}$
14. $100x^5$
15. $x^6$
16. 1
17. 2
18. 1
19. 14
20. 100
21. 7
22. $-2$
23. 16

## Practice 126

a. 2,850 centigrams
b. 17.2 kilograms
c. $-12x^4$
d. 1
e. 19

## Problem Set 126

1. True
2. True
3. 6 pounds
4. 73,600 ounces
5. 3,750 centigrams
6. 14.5 kilograms
7. $8(4 + 19)$

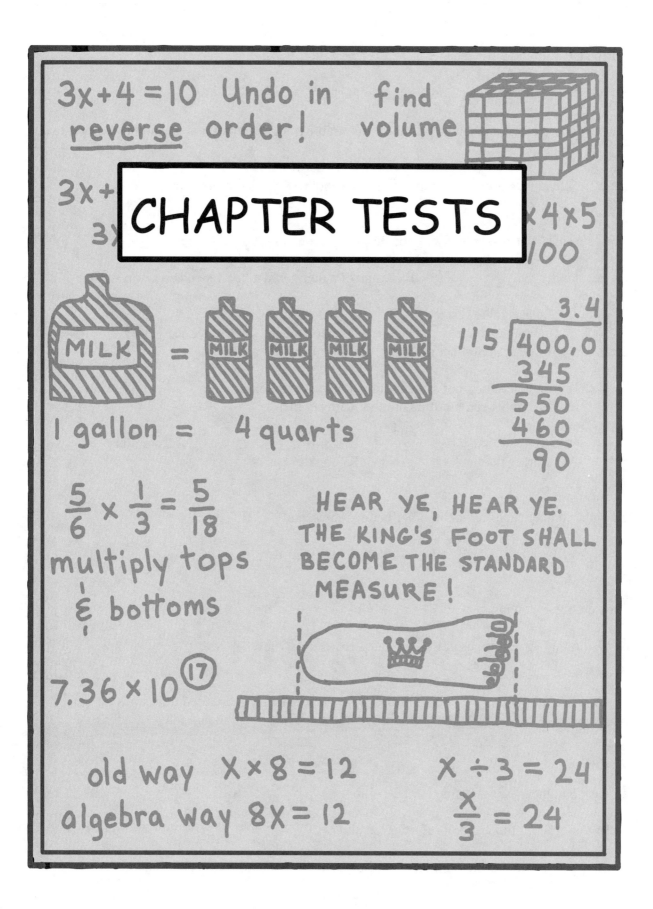

# CHAPTER TESTS

# Chapter 1 Test

Tell whether each sentence below is True or False.

1. The greatest advantage of the Hindu-Arabic (modern) numbers is that they work like an abacus. _True_

2. Moving a number from one column to another is called regrouping. _True_

Complete each sentence below with the best of the choices given.

3. Under the ___A.___ , the value of a number symbol depends on its position.

   A. place value system      B. binary system
   C. Greek alphabet         D. latest scientific discoveries
   E. Egyptian number system

4. If our modern number system did not have a symbol for ___B.___ , it would be easy to confuse one written number with another.

   A. plus             B. zero           C. minus
   D. three          E. equal

Tell what number each Roman number below represents.

5. VIII _8_                         6. DCCLXII _762_

Complete the following.

7. 5,934 = _5_ thousands _9_ hundreds _3_ tens _4_ ones

8. 82,473,186 = _8_ ten millions _2_ millions _4_ hundred thousands _7_ ten thousands _3_ thousands _1_ hundreds _8_ tens _6_ ones

Write each number below (using modern numbers).

9. sixty-four thousand, three hundred eight _64,308_

10. five hundred billion, nineteen million, two hundred thousand, eight hundred seventy
    _500,019,200,870_

Write each number below in words.

**11.** 2,697,004

two million, six hundred ninty-seven thousand, four

**12.** 67,009

sixty-seven thousand, nine

Answer each question below.

**13.** Write a number that is 10,000 greater than 306,984. 316,984

**14.** Write a number that is 1,000 less than 82,577,693. 82,576,693

Rearrange the digits in each number below so that it is as large as possible.

**15.** 803,759: 987,530

**16.** 2,684 : 8,642

**17.** 3,907,501: 9,753,100

Add each group of numbers below.

**18.**
$$\begin{array}{r} 348 \\ +251 \\ \hline 599 \end{array}$$

**19.**
$$\begin{array}{r} 1\phantom{0}1\phantom{0} \\ 15,059 \\ +67,270 \\ \hline 82,329 \end{array}$$

**20.**
$$\begin{array}{r} 1\phantom{0}11 \\ 2,683 \\ 509 \\ +4,034 \\ \hline 7,226 \end{array}$$

Subtract each group of numbers below.

**21.**
$$\begin{array}{r} 55,555 \\ -243 \\ \hline 55,312 \end{array}$$

**22.**
$$\begin{array}{r} 8\phantom{0} \\ \cancel{9}2 \\ -48 \\ \hline 44 \end{array}$$

**23.**
$$\begin{array}{r} 4\phantom{0} \\ 7\cancel{5}1 \\ -146 \\ \hline 605 \end{array}$$

Translate the word problem below into math; then solve.

**24.** Scientists first estimated that the blob weighed 9,542 pounds, but later testing showed that their estimate had been 497 pounds too high. How much does the blob actually weigh? 9,45

## Chapter 2 Test

Tell whether each sentence below is True or False.

1.  Multiplication is really just a shortcut for repeated subtraction. *False*

2.  Division is breaking a total down into groups of different sizes. *false*

Complete each sentence below with the best of the choices given.

3.  In a division problem, the number that you are dividing by is called the _divisor_ .

    A.  divisor      B.  quotient      C.  dividend
    D.  sum          E.  remainder

4.  Any number that ends in _0, 2, 4, 6 or 8_ is called an even number and can be divided evenly by 2.

    A.  5 or 10       B.  0, 2, 4, 6, or 8       C.  9
    D.  0             E.  1

Answer each question below.

5.  Multiply $100,000 \times 659,000$ . *659,00,000,000*

6.  Divide $194,000,000 \div 100,000$ . *1,940*

7.  Tell whether 5,790 can be divided evenly by 3. *yes*

8.  Tell whether 23,986 can be divided evenly by 4. *no*

Add each group of numbers below.

9.
```
   469
 1,356
+9,472
─────
11,297
```

10.
```
 3,047
 8,926
+2,703
─────
14,676
```

11.
```
 2,160
 3,230
 3,406
+1,203
─────
 9,999
```

Subtract each pair of numbers below.

**12.**
$$\begin{array}{r} 297 \\ -194 \\ \hline 103 \end{array}$$

**13.**
$$\begin{array}{r} 88,222 \\ -4,982 \\ \hline 83740 \end{array}$$

**14.**
$$\begin{array}{r} 67,829 \\ -43,280 \\ \hline 24,549 \end{array}$$

Multiply each pair of numbers below.

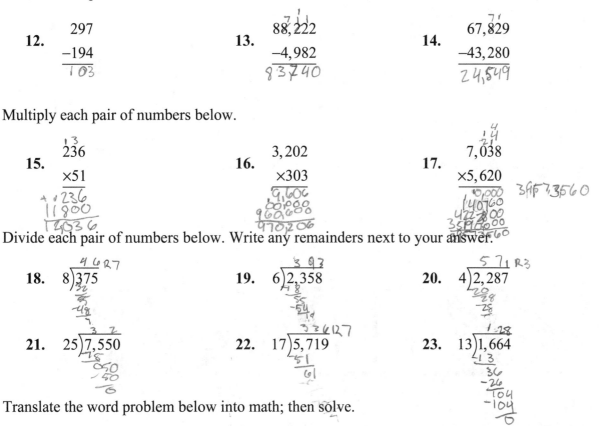

**15.**
$$\begin{array}{r} 236 \\ \times 51 \end{array}$$

**16.**
$$\begin{array}{r} 3,202 \\ \times 303 \end{array}$$

**17.**
$$\begin{array}{r} 7,038 \\ \times 5,620 \end{array}$$

Divide each pair of numbers below. Write any remainders next to your answer.

**18.** 8)375

**19.** 6)2,358

**20.** 4)2,287

**21.** 25)7,550

**22.** 17)5,719

**23.** 13)1,664

Translate the word problem below into math; then solve.

**24.** Mr. Lowell has one of the most impressive antique toy collections in the United States, and he plans to distribute all 34,083 toys in his collection evenly to 21 different museums. How many toys will each museum get? 1,623

49

## Chapter 3 Test

Tell whether each sentence below is True or False.

1. The numerator tells you how many pieces into which the whole has been broken. *true*

2. Multiplying the top and bottom of a fraction by the same number will not change the fraction's value. *true*

3. Rewriting a number as a multiplication is called factoring. *true*

Write a fraction to represent each diagram below.

4. *$\frac{3}{7}$*

5. *$\frac{3}{4}$*

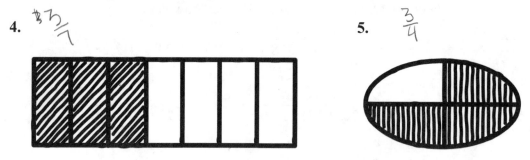

Tell whether a <, >, or = sign should go between these fractions.

6. $\frac{7}{13}$ *>* $\frac{13}{26}$

7. $\frac{5}{7}$ *<* $\frac{4}{5}$

8. $\frac{4}{9}$ *=* $\frac{12}{27}$

Answer each question below.

9. Tell whether 2,985,733 can be divided evenly by 2. *no*

10. Tell whether 87,237 can be divided evenly by 9. *no*

Add each group of numbers below.

11.
$$\begin{array}{r} 5,357 \\ 2,089 \\ +4,768 \\ \hline 12,214 \end{array}$$

12.
$$\begin{array}{r} 3,023 \\ 2,113 \\ 8,401 \\ +3,360 \\ \hline 16,897 \end{array}$$

Subtract each pair of numbers below.

13.
```
   9,478
  −5,243
```
4,235

14.
```
  54,322
  −6,742
```
47,580

Multiply each pair of numbers below.

15.
```
    507
    ×47
```
3549
20280
23829

16.
```
    204
   ×321
```
65,484

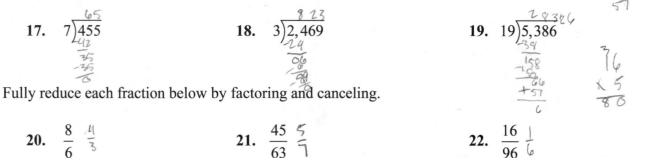

Divide each pair of numbers below. Write any remainders next to your answer.

17. 7)455

18. 3)2,469

19. 19)5,386

Fully reduce each fraction below by factoring and canceling.

20. $\frac{8}{6}$  $\frac{4}{3}$

21. $\frac{45}{63}$  $\frac{5}{7}$

22. $\frac{16}{96}$  $\frac{1}{6}$

23. $\frac{84}{7}$  $\frac{7}{1}$

Translate the word problem below into math; then solve.

24.  Prisoner of war #7 has been told by his buddies to tap the wall 3 times every time the guard walks by. If the prisoner has tapped the wall 516 times today, how many times has the guard walked by? 172

## Chapter 4 Test

Tell whether each sentence below is True or False.

1. To subtract two fractions, subtract their numerators and their denominators. *true*

2. The lowest common denominator (LCD) is the smallest number that the denominators will divide into evenly. *true*

3. A mixed number is a fraction with an odd number numerator and even number denominator. *false*

Add or subtract each group of numbers below.

4. $47,200$
   $-7,201$
   $39,999$

5. $5,360$
   $7,242$
   $2,101$
   $+4,008$
   $18,711$

6. $29,194$
   $-16,378$
   $12,816$

Multiply or divide each pair of numbers below.

7. $621$
   $\times 24$
   $2484$
   $12420$
   $14904$

8. $33\overline{)17,193}$  521
   $165$
   $69$
   $66$
   $33$

9. $905$
   $\times 126$
   $5430$
   $18100$
   $90500$
   $114,030$

Fully reduce each fraction below by factoring and canceling.

10. $\dfrac{14}{86}$  $\dfrac{11}{6}$

11. $\dfrac{45}{25}$  $\dfrac{9}{5} = 1\dfrac{4}{5}$

Find the lowest common denominator for each group of fractions below.

12. $\dfrac{1}{15}, \dfrac{9}{5}, \dfrac{3}{8}$  5

13. $\dfrac{5}{8}, \dfrac{1}{2}, \dfrac{3}{4}$  2

Add each pair of numbers below to get an improper fraction.

14. $2+\dfrac{1}{4}$   $\dfrac{9}{4}$

15. $5+\dfrac{3}{4}$   $\dfrac{23}{4}$

16. $9+\dfrac{2}{3}$   $\dfrac{29}{3}$

Change each improper fraction below into a mixed number.

17. $\dfrac{26}{5}$   $5\dfrac{1}{5}$

18. $\dfrac{103}{7}$   $13\dfrac{1}{7}$

19. $\dfrac{15}{11}$   $1\dfrac{4}{11}$

Add or subtract each pair of numbers below. Make sure your answers are fully reduced.

20. $\dfrac{1}{3}+\dfrac{7}{12}$   $\dfrac{8}{15}$

21. $\dfrac{3}{8}-\dfrac{2}{9}$   $1$

22. $2\dfrac{1}{4}+\dfrac{2}{5}$   $2\dfrac{3}{9}$

Translate the word problem below into math; then solve.

23. When the *Commission for Better Cruises* finally finished its survey, they reported that $\dfrac{1}{6}$ of the passengers complained of sea-sickness, $\dfrac{1}{9}$ were stricken with sunburn, and $\dfrac{1}{18}$ said that shuffleboard was not as fun as they thought it would be. What fraction of the passengers gave one of these three complaints? Be sure to reduce your answer fully.

## Chapter 5 Test

Tell whether each sentence below is True or False.

1. To multiply fractions, just multiply their tops and bottoms.

2. To divide fractions, change the division to multiplication by the reciprocal.

3. To multiply a whole number and fraction, change the multiplication to division and divide normally.

Add or subtract each group of numbers below.

4.
$$
\begin{array}{r}
121 \\
4,852 \\
8,058 \\
+589 \\
\hline
\end{array}
$$

5.
$$
\begin{array}{r}
75,608 \\
-38,002 \\
\hline
\end{array}
$$

Multiply or divide each pair of numbers below.

6.
$$
\begin{array}{r}
1,011 \\
\times 306 \\
\hline
\end{array}
$$

7. $21\overline{)31,472}$

Fully reduce each fraction below by factoring and canceling.

8. $\dfrac{78}{36}$

9. $\dfrac{28}{77}$

Add or subtract each pair of fractions below. Make sure your answers are fully reduced.

10. $\dfrac{3}{9}+\dfrac{2}{9}$

11. $\dfrac{9}{6}-\dfrac{5}{8}$

12. $4\dfrac{1}{3}-2\dfrac{3}{4}$

13. $5\dfrac{3}{4}+\dfrac{5}{2}+\dfrac{7}{8}$

Multiply each pair of numbers below.

**14.** $\dfrac{7}{9} \times 63$

**15.** $\dfrac{7}{45} \times \dfrac{3}{2}$

**16.** $\dfrac{8}{30} \times \dfrac{5}{4}$

Divide each pair of numbers below.

**17.** $\dfrac{1}{7} \div 5$

**18.** $\dfrac{3}{8} \div \dfrac{1}{5}$

**19.** $\dfrac{8}{7} \div \dfrac{8}{21}$

Answer each question below.

**20.** What is $\dfrac{5}{9}$ of 360?

**21.** 200 has how many $\dfrac{1}{4}$s in it?

**22.** What is $\dfrac{2}{3}$ of $\dfrac{9}{12}$?

**23.** 5 has how many $\dfrac{1}{16}$s in it?

Translate the word problem below into math; then solve.

**24.** Bobby hit the wrong lever and as a result the factory produced way too many cheesy puffs. If the factory managers decided to give $\dfrac{1}{3}$ of $\dfrac{1}{9}$ of a ton away as samples, what fraction of a ton did they give away?

## Chapter 6 Test

Tell whether each sentence below is True or False.

    **1.**   Decimals are special fractions that have been designed to fit the abacus system.

    **2.**   Fractions are easier to add and subtract when they are written as decimals.

    **3.**   A decimal that goes on forever is called a terminating decimal.

Write each number below as a decimal.

    **4.**  $\dfrac{66}{100}$
    **5.**  $8\dfrac{15}{1,000}$

Add or subtract each group of numbers below.

**6.**
$$\begin{array}{r} 645.62 \\ +132.15 \\ \hline \end{array}$$

**7.**
$$\begin{array}{r} 38.89 \\ -21.375 \\ \hline \end{array}$$

**8.**
$$\begin{array}{r} 4,139 \\ 7,496 \\ +5,055 \\ \hline \end{array}$$

Multiply or divide each pair of numbers below. Write any remainders in decimal form.

**9.**
$$\begin{array}{r} 201.2 \\ \times 0.1 \\ \hline \end{array}$$

**10.**   $0.5\overline{)55.5}$

**11.**
$$\begin{array}{r} 2,500 \\ \times 15 \\ \hline \end{array}$$

**12.**   $6\overline{)511}$

**13.**
$$\begin{array}{r} 108.2 \\ \times 0.04 \\ \hline \end{array}$$

Add or subtract each pair of fractions below. Make sure your answers are fully reduced.

    **14.**  $3\dfrac{1}{2}+\dfrac{3}{4}$
    **15.**  $\dfrac{12}{10}-\dfrac{2}{5}$

Multiply or divide each pair of numbers below.

**16.**   $\dfrac{5}{8} \div \dfrac{15}{32}$

**17.**   $64 \times \dfrac{3}{8}$

Convert each fraction below into decimal form.

**18.**   $\dfrac{13}{25}$

**19.**   $\dfrac{2}{9}$

Convert each decimal below into a fraction. Make sure your answers are fully reduced.

**20.**   0.25

**21.**   0.125

Round each decimal below to two digits (hundredths).

**22.**   3.14159

**23.**   $0.8\overline{9}$

Translate the word problem below into math; then solve.

**24.**   Hamster Accessories Incorporated sells nine-inch "porch swings" for $9.95 each. If the company sold $527.35 worth of porch swings, how many did they sell?

## Chapter 7 Test

Tell whether each sentence below is True or False.

1. The word percent means "per hundred."

2. To calculate the percent of a number, change the percent to a fraction or decimal and multiply.

Add or subtract each group of numbers below.

3.  
$$\begin{array}{r} 52.05 \\ 25.25 \\ +15.50 \\ \hline \end{array}$$

4.  
$$\begin{array}{r} 63.54 \\ -32.34 \\ \hline \end{array}$$

Multiply or divide each pair of numbers below. Write any remainders in decimal form.

5.  
$$\begin{array}{r} 0.625 \\ \times 0.5 \\ \hline \end{array}$$

6. $0.8\overline{)48.2}$

7.  
$$\begin{array}{r} 2.25 \\ \times 7.4 \\ \hline \end{array}$$

Add or subtract each pair of fractions below. Make sure your answers are fully reduced.

8. $\dfrac{2}{3}+\dfrac{5}{6}$

9. $10-\dfrac{13}{2}$

10. $3\dfrac{2}{8}+2\dfrac{3}{4}$

Multiply or divide each pair of numbers below. Make sure your answers are fully reduced.

11. $\dfrac{15}{21}\times\dfrac{3}{5}$

12. $88\div\dfrac{11}{8}$

Convert each fraction below into decimal form. Round any repeating decimals to two digits (hundredths).

13. $\dfrac{8}{9}$

14. $\dfrac{75}{50}$

Convert each decimal below into a fraction. Make sure your answers are fully reduced.

**15.** 0.33

**16.** 6.44

Convert each percent below into decimal form.

**17.** $22\frac{2}{5}\%$

**18.** 80%

Convert each percent below into a fraction. Make sure your answers are fully reduced.

**19.** 12.5%

**20.** $4\frac{1}{2}\%$

Answer each question below.

**21.** What is $\frac{2}{5}$ of 1,000?

**22.** What is $2\frac{1}{2}\%$ of 25?

**23.** What percent of 120 is 15?

Translate the word problem below into math; then solve.

**24.** Moose plans to eat 8 of his mom's minty macaroons while he's filling up her car with gas. So far he has eaten 6. What percent of his goal has been achieved?

# Chapter 8 Test

Tell whether each sentence below is True or False.

1. Units of measurement were probably first used by bankers to calculate interest rates on loans.

2. The first standards for units of measure were based on the body parts of kings.

Complete each sentence below with the best of the choices given.

3. A meter is equal to 1,000 _____.

      A. kilometers     B. hectometers     C. dekameters
      D. centimeters     E. millimeters

4. 10 centimeters equals 1 _____.

      A. kilometer     B. dekameter     C. meter
      D. decimeter     E. centimeter

5. A kilometer is equal to 100 _____.

      A. hectometers     B. decimeters     C. meters
      D. dekameters     E. centimeters

Multiply or divide each pair of numbers below. Write any remainders in decimal form.

6.
$$\begin{array}{r} 250 \\ \times 2.2 \\ \hline \end{array}$$

7. $25\overline{)20,250}$

Add or subtract each pair of fractions below. Make sure your answers are fully reduced.

8. $\dfrac{3}{7} + \dfrac{3}{5}$

9. $\dfrac{5}{8} - \dfrac{1}{3}$

Multiply or divide each pair of numbers below.

10. $\dfrac{3}{4} \times 2\dfrac{2}{5}$

11. $5 \div \dfrac{25}{10}$

Convert each decimal below into a fraction. Make sure your answers are fully reduced.

**12.** 0.625

**13.** 0.8

Convert each percent below into decimal form.

**14.** $4\frac{7}{20}\%$

**15.** 85%

Do each unit conversion below. (common system conversion factors: 12 inches = 1 foot; 3 feet = 1 yard; 1,760 yards = 1 mile.)

**16.** Convert 26 yards 122 feet to inches.

**17.** How many meters are in 50 decimeters?

Do each unit conversion below. (common-metric conversion factors: 39.37 inches = 1 meter; 1 inch = 2.54 centimeters; 1.0936 yards = 1 meter; 1 mile = 1.609 kilometer)

**18.** Convert 10 miles to kilometers.

**19.** Convert 20 decimeters to inches. Round your answer to two digits (hundredths).

Answer each question below.

**20.** What is $\frac{3}{7}$ of 56?

**21.** What is 35% of 82?

**22.** What percent of 90 is 22.5?

**23.** $\frac{3}{4}$ has how many $\frac{1}{8}$ s in it?

Translate the word problem below into math; then solve.

**24.** Last year, Frankie's Deli made an 11 foot 6 inch submarine sandwich (just for kicks). This year, they plan to make another one 2 feet and 3 inches longer (a size that will cover their entire front counter). How many <u>feet</u> long will this sandwich be?

## Chapter 9 Test

Tell whether each sentence below is True or False.

1. A flat surface or "area" is measured by determining how many little squares will fit on it.

2. A three-dimensional (3D) space is measured by figuring out how many little cubes will fit inside of it.

Complete each sentence below with the best of the choices given.

3. 1 *square* kilometer equals 100 _____.

   A. square dekameters       B. square hectometers
   C. square millimeters       D. square decimeters
   E. square centimeters

4. 1,000 *cubic* centimeters equals 1 _____.

   A. cubic kilometer       B. cubic hectometer
   C. cubic dekameter       D. cubic decimeter
   E. cubic centimeter

5. 1,000 liters equals 1 _____.

   A. kiloliter       B. hectoliter
   C. dekaliter       D. deciliter
   E. centiliter

Add or subtract each group of numbers below.

6.  $\begin{array}{r} 23,106 \\ +27,648 \\ \hline \end{array}$

7.  $\begin{array}{r} 0.867 \\ -0.35 \\ \hline \end{array}$

Multiply or divide each pair of numbers below. Write any remainders in decimal form.

8.  $\begin{array}{r} 4.55 \\ \times 7 \\ \hline \end{array}$

9.  $5\overline{)976}$

Add or subtract each pair of fractions below. Make sure your answers are fully reduced.

10. $\dfrac{3}{21} + \dfrac{4}{21}$ 　　　　 11. $1\dfrac{3}{5} - \dfrac{1}{4}$

Multiply or divide each pair of numbers below.

12. $\dfrac{6}{25} \times \dfrac{5}{3}$ 　　　　 13. $\dfrac{5}{7} \div 35$

Convert each fraction below into decimal form. Give exact answers (no rounding).

14. $\dfrac{3}{25}$ 　　　　 15. $\dfrac{1}{36}$

Answer each question below.

16. What is $\dfrac{3}{13}$ of 156? 　　　　 17. How many $\dfrac{1}{3}$ s are in 6?

18. What percent of 1,200 is 240?

Do each unit conversion below.

19. How many square feet are in 14 square yards?

20. Convert 3,250 liters to hectoliters.

21. How many fluid ounces are in 8 pints? (1 gallon = 4 quarts; 1 quart = 2 pints; 1 pint = 16 fluid ounces)

22. How many cubic feet are in 3,456 cubic inches?

23. Convert 5 yards to inches.

Translate the word problem below into math; then solve.

24. Super Duper Saver Grocery plans to build a new wing onto one of its many gigantic distribution centers. The facility will hold 100,000 cubic meters of *Soon-to-be-Black* brand bananas. How many cubic decimeters is this?

## Chapter 10 Test

Tell whether each sentence below is True or False.

1. In algebra problems, the missing number is mixed together with other numbers.

2. The golden rule of algebra says that if you change the value of one side of an equation, the value of the other side must be changed by the same amount.

Complete each sentence below with the best of the choices given.

3. A group of numbers and $x$'s is called a (or an) _____.

    A. equation          B. solution          C. paragraph
    D. expression       E. multiplication

4. The answer to an equation is also called the _____.

    A. expression       B. tabulation       C. exception
    D. solution           E. sum

5. Two operations that can undo each other are called _____ operations.

    A. solution         B. expression       C. algebra
    D. inverse           E. arithmetic

Add or subtract each group of numbers below.

6.
$$\begin{array}{r} 42 \\ 17.5 \\ +60.2 \\ \hline \end{array}$$

7.
$$\begin{array}{r} 63.2 \\ -39.4 \\ \hline \end{array}$$

Multiply or divide each pair of numbers below. Write any remainders in decimal form.

8.
$$\begin{array}{r} 31.4 \\ \times 1.5 \\ \hline \end{array}$$

9. $3.6\overline{)8,530}$

Add or subtract each pair of fractions below. Make sure your answers are fully reduced.

**10.** $\dfrac{3}{4} + \dfrac{1}{10}$

**11.** $\dfrac{3}{5} - \dfrac{2}{9}$

Convert each fraction below into decimal form. Give exact answers (no rounding).

**12.** $\dfrac{1}{3}$

**13.** $\dfrac{3}{16}$

Do each unit conversion below.

**14.** How many feet are in 306 inches?

**15.** Convert 1,375 square meters to square dekameters.

Answer each question below.

**16.** What must be done to the expression $x \times 89$ to make it equal $x$?

**17.** How far will a cyclist riding at 25 miles per hour travel in 3.5 hours?

Solve each equation below by undoing.

**18.** $x + 4 = 13.5$

**19.** $25x = 525$

**20.** $\dfrac{x}{12} = 101$

**21.** $\dfrac{4}{15}x = \dfrac{2}{5}$

**22.** $x - \dfrac{1}{6} = \dfrac{1}{12}$

Translate the word problem below into an equation; then solve.

**23.** The third shipment weighed 10.25 times as much as the second shipment. If the third shipment weighed 15,662 pounds, how much did the second shipment weigh?

## Chapter 11 Test

Tell whether each sentence below is True or False.

**1.** The positive whole numbers, negative whole numbers, and zero are together called "integers."

**2.** When multiplying with negatives, if the signs are different, the answer is always positive, and if the signs are the same, the answer is always negative.

Multiply or divide each pair of fractions below. Make sure your answers are fully reduced.

**3.** $\dfrac{10}{45} \cdot \dfrac{9}{6}$

**4.** $\dfrac{21}{8} \div \dfrac{7}{12}$

Do each unit conversion below.

**5.** Convert 12 decimeters to millimeters.

**6.** How many cubic yards are in 1,215 cubic feet?

Answer each question below.

**7.** What is $\dfrac{3}{7}$ of 49?

**8.** What is $\dfrac{1}{3}$ of $\dfrac{6}{11}$?

Add each pair of numbers below.

**9.** $-4 + (-36)$

**10.** $-11 + 4$

Subtract each pair of numbers below.

**11.** $14 - (-6)$

**12.** $-25 - (-17)$

Multiply each pair of numbers below.

**13.** $(-7)(65)$

**14.** $(-20)(-15)$

Divide each pair of numbers below.

**15.** $\dfrac{-91}{7}$

**16.** $\dfrac{-45}{-9}$

Tell whether each of the following pairs of expressions is equivalent.

**17.** $-15+x$ and $-x-15$

**18.** $\dfrac{-33}{x}$ and $\dfrac{33}{-x}$

Solve each equation below by undoing.

**19.** $x+54=-6$

**20.** $-\dfrac{8}{5}x=56$

**21.** $\dfrac{x}{-40}=-9$

**22.** $-x-17=-63$

**23.** $\dfrac{x}{8}=\dfrac{3}{4}$

Translate the word problem below into an equation; then solve.

**24.** Ninety-eight percent of the mules who were surveyed said that stubbornness was a good character trait. If 343 mules gave this response, how many were surveyed in total?

## Chapter 12 Test

Tell whether each sentence below is True or False.

1. Multiplication and division should be done before addition and subtraction, unless indicated differently by parentheses or a fraction bar.

2. When solving an equation with two operations, you should undo the operations in reverse order.

Add or subtract each group of numbers below.

3.
$$\begin{array}{r} 23.58 \\ +67.53 \\ \hline \end{array}$$

4.
$$\begin{array}{r} 74.68 \\ -52.46 \\ \hline \end{array}$$

Add or subtract (as indicated) each pair of numbers below.

5. $75+(-25)$

6. $-68-(-34)$

Multiply or divide (as indicated) each pair of numbers below.

7. $(4)(-75)$

8. $\dfrac{21}{-3}$

Calculate the value of each expression below. (Make sure to do the operations in the correct order.)

9. $-\dfrac{45}{5}+21$

10. $12+9\cdot2$

11. $-3(4+3)$

Translate each of the following phrases into a mathematical expression. (Don't calculate the answer.)

12. $-8$ subtracted from 4 first, and then that total divided by 4.

13. 5 multiplied by 9 first, and then 6 added to that total.

Translate each of the following word problems into an equation. (Don't solve.)

14. There's some number that if you multiply it by $-34$ first, and then subtract 5 from that total, the result is 64.

15. There's some number that if you subtract 78 from it first, and then multiply that total by 9, the result is 108.

Simplify each expression below.

16. $4+9x+7$

17. $2-7x-9$

18. $\dfrac{3}{8}+9x-\dfrac{1}{2}$

Solve each equation below by undoing.

19. $4x+(-12)=8$

20. $6+\dfrac{-x}{2}=14$

21. $-3+5x-7=-20$

22. $-3(x-14)=42$

23. $2-x+4=5$

Translate the word problem below into an equation; then solve.

24. There is a number that if you add 5 to it first, and then divide that total by 3, you get 12. What's the number?

## Chapter 13 Test

Tell whether each sentence below is True or False.

**1.** A number multiplied by an $x$ is called a "coefficient."

**2.** To solve an equation with $x$'s on both sides, you have to cancel the $x$'s.

Convert each percent below into decimal form.

**3.** 36.45%          **4.** 24%

Answer each question below.

**5.** What is 30% of 145?

**6.** What is $\dfrac{3}{4}$ of $\dfrac{8}{21}$ ?

Add or subtract (as indicated) each pair of numbers below.

**7.** $-(-25)-15$          **8.** $18+(-13)$

Multiply or divide (as indicated) each pair of numbers below.

**9.** $\dfrac{-39}{-13}$          **10.** $(-4)(8.25)$

Calculate the value of each expression below. (Make sure to do the operations in the correct order.)

**11.** $(7)(-8)+6$          **12.** $\dfrac{3-(-9)}{2}$

Translate each of the following phrases into a mathematical expression. (Don't calculate the answer.)

**13.**  −35 added to −48 first, and then that total divided by 6.

**14.**  16 divided by −4 first, and 36 added to that total.

Translate each of the following word problems into an equation. (Don't solve.)

**15.**  There's some number that if you add 38 to it first, and then multiply that total by −14, the result is 55.

**16.**  There's some number that if you divide it by 4 first, and then add 26 to that total, the result is 89.

Simplify each expression below.

**17.**  $5x - 2x$  **18.**  $-16x + 11x$

Solve each equation below.

**19.**  $13 - 5x = -12$   **20.**  $\dfrac{-3x + 9}{3} = 6$   **21.**  $-2x + 4x = 16$

**22.**  $-12x + (-8x) = -140$   **23.**  $21 - 3x = 10 + 8x$

Translate the word problem below into an equation; then solve.

**24.**  Motor scooter #1 and motor scooter #2 are headed straight toward each other. Scooter #1 is traveling at 22 mph, and scooter #2 is traveling at 24 mph. If the two scooters are 92 miles apart, how many hours will it be before they meet?

## Chapter 14 Test

Tell whether each sentence below is True or False.

**1.** To reduce fractions with $x$'s, you factor and cancel.

**2.** An $x$ is treated as a prime number when factoring.

Add or subtract (as indicated) each pair of numbers below.

**3.** $-2.5 + (-3.5)$

**4.** $22 - (-5)$

Multiply or divide (as indicated) each group of numbers below.

**5.** $\dfrac{42}{-6}$

**6.** $(3)(-10)(4)$

Calculate the value of each expression below. (Make sure to do the operations in the correct order.)

**7.** $-6 - \dfrac{24}{4}$

**8.** $-3(-16 - 14)$

Translate each of the following word problems into an equation. (Don't solve.)

**9.** There's some number that if you add 46 to it first, and then divide that total by 5, the result is 19.

**10.** There's some number that if you multiply it by 6 first, and then subtract 14 from that total, the result is 256.

Simplify each expression below.

**11.** $-13x - (-27x)$

**12.** $-x + 8x$

Reduce each fraction below.

**13.** $\dfrac{16}{8(x-4)}$

**14.** $\dfrac{7(x+5)}{35(x+5)}$

Multiply or divide (as indicated) each pair of fractions below. (Make sure your answers are fully reduced.)

**15.** $\dfrac{12x}{45x} \cdot \dfrac{20}{6x}$

**16.** $\dfrac{10}{3x} \div \dfrac{55}{9x}$

Add each pair of fractions below. (Make sure your answers are fully reduced.)

**17.** $\dfrac{1}{7x} + \dfrac{6}{7x}$

**18.** $\dfrac{5}{6x} + \dfrac{1}{3x}$

Subtract each pair of fractions below.

**19.** $\dfrac{1}{3x} - \dfrac{5}{3x}$

**20.** $\dfrac{3x}{2} - \dfrac{7x}{8}$

Solve each equation below.

**21.** $5(x+6) = 75$

**22.** $-7x + 3x = -28$

**23.** $25 - 7x = 1 + 5x$

Translate the word problem below into an equation; then solve.

**24.** The Pest Patrol only charges $30 for a service call (just to come to the house) plus $20 per hour to do the job. The Bug Stoppers charge $40 for a service call plus $15 per hour to do the job. How many hours would a job have to take for the bills of both services to be the same?

## Chapter 15 Test

Tell whether each sentence below is True or False.

**1.** Raising a number to a power is a short way to write the same number multiplied repeatedly.

**2.** A root is shown with the symbol $\sqrt{\phantom{x}}$ , which is called a radical sign.

Calculate the value of each expression below. (Make sure to do the operations in the correct order.)

**3.** $4^2 - 14$

**4.** $(7-2)^2$

Translate each of the following word problems into an equation. (Don't solve.)

**5.** There's some number that if you subtract 40 from it first, and then multiply that total by 12, the result is 111.

**6.** There's some number that if you divide it by 1.2 first, and then add 42.5 to that total, the result is $-25.5$.

Simplify each expression below.

**7.** $4x^{11} - 3x^{11}$

**8.** $-6x^7 + 12x^7$

Simplify each expression below by multiplying the powers.

**9.** $x^{10} \cdot x^3$

**10.** $10x^2(-2x^6)$

Simplify each expression below by dividing the powers.

**11.** $\dfrac{x^8}{x^3}$

**12.** $\dfrac{x^{12}}{x^3}$

Reduce each fraction below.

**13.** $\dfrac{25x^7}{25x^4}$   **14.** $\dfrac{6x^{10}}{42x^2}$

Multiply or divide (as indicated) each pair of fractions below. Make sure your answers are fully reduced.

**15.** $\dfrac{3x}{8} \div \dfrac{9x}{24}$   **16.** $\dfrac{5x^8}{6} \cdot \dfrac{9}{25x^6}$

Add or subtract (as indicated) each pair of fractions below. (Make sure your answers are fully reduced.)

**17.** $\dfrac{4}{21x} - \dfrac{10}{21x}$   **18.** $\dfrac{2}{9x} + \dfrac{1}{3x}$

Calculate the value of each expression below.

**19.** $\sqrt{6^2}$   **20.** $\sqrt{81}$

Solve each equation below.

**21.** $7x - 2x = 55$   **22.** $\dfrac{x-14}{-4} = 3$

**23.** $12 - 3x = 4 + (-2x)$

Translate the word problem below into an equation; then solve.

**24.** Speed typist #1 can type 95 words each minute. Speed typist #2 can type 98 words each minute. Working together, how many minutes will it take them to type 2,895 words?

## Additional Topics Test

Tell whether each sentence below is True or False.

1. Any number with an exponent of 1 equals the number itself, and any number with an exponent of 0 equals 1.

2. The most popular units from the common (avoirdupois) system for mass are the ounce, the pound, and the ton.

Do each unit conversion below.

3. Convert a mass of 1.5 pounds to ounces.

4. How many pounds are in a mass of 4 tons?

5. Convert a mass of 125 hectograms to decigrams.

6. How many kilograms are in a mass of 160,000 centigrams?

Translate each of the following phrases into a mathematical expression. (Don't calculate the answer.)

7. 23 added to 5 first, and that total multiplied by 7.

8. 1,250 divided by 5 first, and 445 subtracted from that total.

Multiply or divide (as indicated) each pair of fractions below. Make sure your answers are fully reduced.

9. $\dfrac{63x}{21} \cdot \dfrac{42x}{9x}$

10. $\dfrac{9}{8x^2} \div \dfrac{36}{2x^5}$

Simplify each expression below by adding the powers.

11. $15x^8 + 25x^8$

12. $-7x^3 + 3x^3$

Simplify each expression below by multiplying the powers.

**13.** $x \cdot x^9$

**14.** $(5x^4)(7x^5)$

Simplify each expression below by dividing the powers.

**15.** $\dfrac{x^{17}}{x^{17}}$

**16.** $\dfrac{3^{12}}{3^{10}}$

Calculate each root below.

**17.** $\sqrt{1}$

**18.** $\sqrt[4]{81}$

Calculate the value of each expression below.

**19.** $\sqrt[3]{572^3}$

**20.** $(\sqrt{10,000})^2$

Solve each equation below.

**21.** $55 = 5(x+1)$

**22.** $\dfrac{x-8}{3} = -5$

**23.** $7 + 8x = 13 + 5x$

Translate the word problem below into an equation; then solve.

**24.** There is a number that if you multiply it by 8 first, and then subtract 5 from the result, you get 107. What's the number?

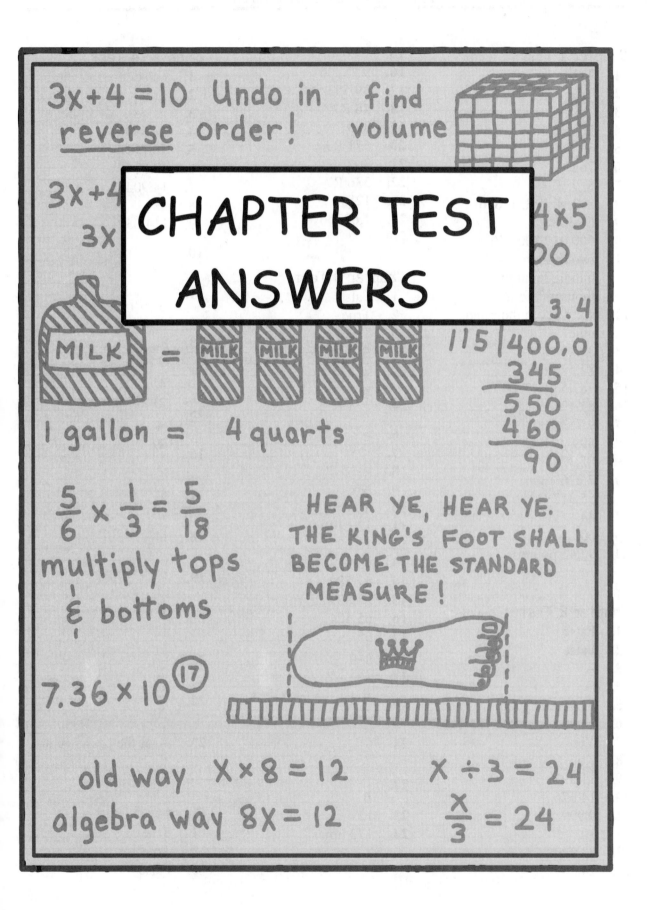

# CHAPTER TEST ANSWERS

$3x + 4 = 10$   Undo in   find
<u>reverse</u> order!   volume

$3x + 4$

$3x$

MILK $=$ MILK MILK MILK MILK

1 gallon $=$ 4 quarts

4×5
00

3.4
$115\overline{)400,0}$
345
550
460
90

$\dfrac{5}{6} \times \dfrac{1}{3} = \dfrac{5}{18}$

multiply tops
& bottoms

HEAR YE, HEAR YE.
THE KING'S FOOT SHALL
BECOME THE STANDARD
MEASURE !

$7.36 \times 10^{\text{⑰}}$

old way   $X \times 8 = 12$         $X \div 3 = 24$
algebra way   $8X = 12$         $\dfrac{X}{3} = 24$

## Chapter 1 Test

1. True
2. True
3. A
4. B
5. 8
6. 762
7. 5, 9, 3, 4
8. 8, 2, 4, 7, 3, 1, 8, 6
9. 64,308
10. 500,019,200,870
11. two million, six hundred ninety-seven thousand, four
12. sixty-seven thousand, nine
13. 316,984
14. 82,576,693
15. 987,530
16. 8,642
17. 9,753,100
18. 599
19. 82,329
20. 7,226
21. 55,312
22. 44
23. 605
24. 9,045 pounds

## Chapter 2 Test

1. False
2. False
3. A
4. B
5. 65,900,000,000
6. 1,940
7. Yes
8. No
9. 11,297
10. 14,676
11. 9,999
12. 103
13. 83,240
14. 24,549
15. 12,036
16. 970,206
17. 39,553,560
18. 46 R7
19. 393
20. 571 R3
21. 302
22. 336 R7
23. 128
24. 1,623 toys

## Chapter 3 Test

1. False
2. True
3. True
4. $\dfrac{3}{7}$
5. $\dfrac{3}{4}$
6. >
7. <
8. =
9. No
10. Yes
11. 12,214
12. 16,897
13. 4,235
14. 47,580
15. 23,829
16. 65,484
17. 65
18. 823
19. 283 R9
20. $\dfrac{4}{3}$
21. $\dfrac{5}{7}$
22. $\dfrac{1}{6}$
23. 12
24. 172 times

## Chapter 4 Test

1. False
2. True
3. False
4. 39,999
5. 18,711
6. 12,816
7. 14,904
8. 521
9. 114,030
10. $\dfrac{7}{43}$
11. $\dfrac{9}{5}$
12. 120
13. 8
14. $\dfrac{9}{4}$
15. $\dfrac{23}{4}$
16. $\dfrac{29}{3}$
17. $5\dfrac{1}{5}$
18. $14\dfrac{5}{7}$
19. $1\dfrac{4}{11}$
20. $\dfrac{11}{12}$
21. $\dfrac{11}{72}$
22. $\dfrac{53}{20}$
23. $\dfrac{1}{3}$ of the passengers

## Chapter 5 Test

1. True
2. True
3. False

4. 13,620
5. 37,606
6. 309,366
7. 1,498 R14
8. $\dfrac{13}{6}$
9. $\dfrac{4}{11}$
10. $\dfrac{5}{9}$
11. $\dfrac{7}{8}$
12. $\dfrac{19}{12}$
13. $\dfrac{73}{8}$
14. 49
15. $\dfrac{7}{30}$
16. $\dfrac{1}{3}$
17. $\dfrac{1}{35}$
18. $\dfrac{15}{8}$
19. 3
20. 200
21. 800
22. $\dfrac{1}{2}$
23. 80
24. $\dfrac{1}{27}$ of a ton

## Chapter 6 Test

1. True
2. True
3. False
4. 0.66
5. 8.015
6. 777.77

7. 17.515
8. 16,690
9. 20.12
10. 111
11. 37,500
12. $85.1\overline{6}$
13. 4.328
14. $\dfrac{17}{4}$
15. $\dfrac{4}{5}$
16. $\dfrac{4}{3}$
17. 24
18. 0.52
19. $0.\overline{2}$
20. $\dfrac{1}{4}$
21. $\dfrac{1}{8}$
22. 3.14
23. 0.90
24. 53 porch swings

## Chapter 7 Test

1. True
2. True
3. 92.80
4. 31.20
5. 0.3125
6. 60.25
7. 16.65
8. $\dfrac{3}{2}$
9. $\dfrac{7}{2}$
10. 6
11. $\dfrac{3}{7}$
12. 64
13. 0.89
14. 1.5

15. $\dfrac{33}{100}$
16. $\dfrac{161}{25}$
17. 0.224
18. 0.8
19. $\dfrac{1}{8}$
20. $\dfrac{9}{200}$
21. 400
22. 0.625
23. 12.5%
24. 75%

## Chapter 8 Test

1. False
2. True
3. E
4. D
5. D
6. 550
7. 810
8. $\dfrac{36}{35}$
9. $\dfrac{7}{24}$
10. $\dfrac{9}{5}$
11. 2
12. $\dfrac{5}{8}$
13. $\dfrac{4}{5}$
14. 0.0435
15. 0.85
16. 2,400 inches
17. 5 meters
18. 16.09 kilometers
19. 78.74 inches
20. 24
21. 28.7

**22.** 25%

**23.** 6

**24.** 13.75 feet or $13\frac{3}{4}$ feet

## Chapter 9 Test
1. True
2. True
3. B
4. D
5. A
6. 50,754
7. 0.517
8. 31.85
9. 195.2
10. $\frac{1}{3}$
11. $\frac{27}{20}$
12. $\frac{2}{5}$
13. $\frac{1}{49}$
14. 0.12
15. $0.02\overline{7}$
16. 36
17. 18
18. 20%
19. 126 square feet
20. 32.5 hectoliters
21. 128 fluid ounces
22. 2 cubic feet
23. 180 inches
24. 100,000,000 cubic decimeters

## Chapter 10 Test
1. True
2. True
3. D
4. D
5. D

6. 119.7
7. 23.8
8. 47.1
9. $2,369.\overline{4}$
10. $\frac{17}{20}$
11. $\frac{17}{45}$
12. $0.\overline{3}$
13. 0.1875
14. 25.5 feet
15. 13.75 square dekameters
16. Divide by 89
17. 87.5 miles
18. 9.5
19. 21
20. 1,212
21. $\frac{3}{2}$
22. $\frac{1}{4}$
23. 1,528 pounds

## Chapter 11 Test
1. True
2. False
3. $\frac{1}{3}$
4. $\frac{9}{2}$
5. 1,200 millimeters
6. 45 cubic yards
7. 21
8. $\frac{2}{11}$
9. −40
10. −7
11. 20
12. −8
13. −455
14. 300

15. −13
16. 5
17. No
18. Yes
19. −60
20. −35
21. 360
22. 46
23. 6
24. 350 mules

## Chapter 12 Test
1. True
2. True
3. 91.11
4. 22.22
5. 50
6. −34
7. −300
8. −7
9. 12
10. 30
11. −21
12. $\frac{4-(-8)}{4}$
13. $5 \cdot 9 + 6$
14. $-34x - 5 = 64$
15. $9(x - 78) = 108$
16. $9x + 11$
17. $-7x + (-7)$
18. $9x + \left(-\frac{1}{8}\right)$
19. 5
20. −16
21. −2
22. 0
23. 1
24. 31

## Chapter 13 Test
1. True
2. False